3.95

C000263939

LIFE IS AN AUSTIN SEVEN

COPING WITH CANCER AND CHEMO

A personal encounter

MIKE STICKLAND

Cover photograph
ACE/SUPERSTOCK

Copyright © 1994 Mike Stickland

ISBN 1 873796 43 9

Published by
AUTUMN HOUSE LIMITED
ALMA PARK, GRANTHAM, LINCS., NG31 9SL

DEDICATION

To my wife, Sheila, with my appreciation
and love;

To my sons Nathan, Bob and Danny,
whom I love with my life and of whom I
am immensely proud;

To Pete and Pat, our friends, who have
done so much for our boys, especially while
we have been 'up north'.

CONTENTS

Sons Nathan, Bob and Danny.

Paradise interrupted

'This table can go next.'

Ten excited and hungry children surged down the dining-room towards the serving-hatch. It was Family Camp at 'Glan Yr Afon', a camp site for Christian youth at Aberdaron on the Lleyn Peninsula in North Wales.

It is a beautiful site in beautiful surroundings. For many dozens of families and hundreds of young people it is almost a paradise on earth; a place to break away from the intensity of life, to make and meet friends and to discover or recharge their faith.

I was on duty that lunch time, controlling which tables could go for food next and generally trying to keep things in order. With 130 hungry bodies, it was important to do things in a disciplined way. And, believe me, it is not always the children who want to jump the queue!

As campers returned with laden plates, I could see that the cooks had excelled themselves again. The wholesome, appetizing meal was being consumed with appreciation; and already those tables which had gone first were beginning to look for second helpings.

Family Camp provides a wonderful 'pot pourri' of campers, ranging from young couples with babies in arms, to mature couples with teenagers no longer interested in sitting with Mum and Dad but wanting to crowd together on teen tables. There were a few single-parent families, too, and the full camp complement was made up by a number of adult volunteers, young and old, working on the staff.

I was enjoying being back in the camping scene. Having entered the ministry in 1969, I had been quickly introduced to the summer youth camp programme by Rex, Doug and Jim; and for more than twenty years I had found

7

satisfaction and fulfilment in the demanding schedules of youth camps and weekend youth retreats.

Every season since 1982 I had been responsible for planning and running camps in many parts of the UK; but in 1990 I had been asked to serve as a conference president in the north of England, and that administrative role had taken me out of the camping programme. Now it was good to be away from my desk again, working on a different 'cutting edge' with vibrant and excited children and their parents.

But, somehow, when it came my turn to eat the meal, I felt that I couldn't face it. It tasted good. It looked good, too. But my appetite had disappeared about a month before, and every mouthful was a trial. That had tended to be the pattern for several days. For one or two days I would feel good, but then pains would come in my right side. There would be a debilitated feeling with loss of appetite followed by vomiting. Then there would be a few hours feeling like a wrung-out dishcloth. I had lost between 15 and 20 pounds in weight in those few weeks.

That afternoon I just had to rest while the remainder of the camp went off to the beach. I felt too ill, and much as I wanted to be with the action, I just couldn't manage it. An hour or so later, what little lunch I had consumed had been vomited back again.

I stayed off duty the rest of that day, but by morning I was feeling good again; and so I was up and about helping to run the camp. The role of camp master that I held was a nice one because there were so many willing helpers to share the load and carry responsibility. In fact, they were all so good that the camp seemed virtually to run itself.

As I walked down the camp field that bright and promising Monday morning, Tony noticed the way I walked, slightly hunched, and holding my right side. 'Mike, I reckon you've got appendicitis,' he said as he approached.

He gently pressed my abdomen, then sharply removed his hand and listened to my gasp of pain.

Tony was our site manager at Glan Yr Afon; and though not able to give professional advice, he 'knew a man who could'. 'Why not get Andrew to have a look at you?' he suggested.

Andrew and Eileen are husband and wife, both consultants in their specialized fields and working in hospitals in Manchester. Since Andrew is a consultant surgeon on site with his family as campers, it certainly made sense to see if he could check me over and give me his opinion.

I went to my caravan to wait while a message was sent up the field to see if he was available. Little did I realize that by evening my taste of that little paradise on earth would be interrupted by a hasty return to Nottingham for urgent medical attention.

The story so far

Within minutes, Andrew was at the door of my caravan. He stepped inside and began by asking me a series of questions about my medical history. I had been a cancer patient in the past and, knowing a little of that, Andrew wished to have the details of the picture filled in before a physical examination.

It all started in 1965. A few months before my twenty-first birthday, I was with Sheila on holiday in Norfolk. At that time she was just my girl-friend. Sheila was brave enough to become my wife in 1966. Now we are in our twenty-ninth year of marriage and have three fine sons of whom we are immensely proud.

We had been to the beach for the day at Great Yarmouth, had soaked up the sun for most of the day and had then decided to walk along the promenade to the fun-fair. But, mysteriously, I found I could walk for only some 100 metres before I felt too ill to carry on. My whole stomach and intestine felt as though it was sinking through my pelvis.

We returned early by train to Sheila's parents' home in Norwich, and travelled on by coach to my parents in Bedfordshire. Mum was so anxious about my condition that she insisted that Dad should take me down to the hospital. There they decided I had been in the sun too long, and that I would be all right in the morning.

But I wasn't!

A visit to the family GP introduced me to a new word, epididymitis. One of my testes was swollen, but a few days on some pills, it was claimed, would set me right and I could return to Newbold College in Berkshire. Here I was due to enter my third year of study in preparation for the ministry.

In the event, I returned to Newbold three weeks late for the new term, but quickly felt ill again. The college GP got on to it fast. Within days I had been referred to the surgeon at Heatherwood Hospital in Ascot, surgery had been completed, and I was peeking at the confidential notes left on the end of my bed by the nurse (as they usually were in those days) in anticipation of the surgeon's rounds.

What I saw when I peeked confirmed my worst suspicions. The college GP had suggested a number of explanations for my continued epididymitis, including tuberculosis and cancer. In the heart of a wordy pathological report, much of which I could not understand, I saw the words underlined in red: *malignant tumour.* I wondered whether the surgeon would admit that or try to keep it secret.

When I asked him what they had found, the surgeon came up close to my side and said, 'We have removed your left testis. You have cancer. You will need some radiotherapy treatment to try to destroy any malignant cells remaining, and then we shall just have to see how it goes.'

I was relieved that he had chosen to tell me frankly. Had he concealed the truth at that point, it would have troubled me deeply. Much later I found out that the medical term for my malignancy was 'teratoma' — the same form of cancer I believe that jockey Bob Champion and footballer Bobby Moore had at about the same time.

By that time in my life I had been a Christian for some two-and-a-half years. My family was firmly Christian-oriented though we seldom attended church as a family. My sisters and I did attend Sunday school at the local Congregational church, and my father was always a deeply spiritual man; though, as I say, he seldom attended church. More of him and his faith later.

Having left school after 'O' levels, I joined the Norfolk Constabulary as a cadet. Simultaneously, a door-to-door salesman of Christian books called at our home. First my dad and sister, then I and other members of my family started to attend a new church in Norwich, in which city I was born and raised. A couple of years later I had made my decision to be baptized, to leave the police force, and to train for the ministry.

God used the few weeks when I was laid up in bed awaiting diagnosis and surgery, to do something very special. He prompted me to do a lot of reading — from my Bible and from various devotional books. That produced within me a calm peace; such that when the surgeon told me, 'You have cancer', it was not overwhelming or threatening at all. I knew that I was in God's hands, and that I had no intention of taking myself out of His care.

I did not know that I would be healed. I *did* know that God had power to heal me via the miracle of modern medicine or, if He chose, by some directly miraculous intervention. Or He might allow me to pass to my rest. Somehow, by God's gracious gift of peace, I wasn't troubled.

There was a huge prayer support from my fellow-students at Newbold College, and from churches and members in different parts of the UK. Their faith and prayers meant a great deal.

Ever since 23 December 1965, when I finally completed six weeks of radiotherapy at six minutes a day, I have been able to praise God for life and the opportunity to serve Him. There was one brief period of concern in December 1971 when it appeared the cancer might have returned, but it turned out to be scar tissue caused by the radiotherapy. Once it was removed by surgery, everything returned to normal.

I conveyed the medical aspects of the 1965 and 1971 episodes to Andrew; then I had to tell him about a second brush with cancer I had had during 1988. By that time I had been serving as a national director for youth ministries from an office based in Watford.

Returning from Pakistan late in January '88, having

been involved with Jim Huzzey in a European youth project, building two churches in Punjabi villages, I remember standing before my mirror at home, glad to be able to trim my beard after some weeks away; and as I did so I noticed a gland in my neck just very slightly swollen.

The next day when I visited my GP he told me he thought there was nothing to worry about, until I told him of my teratoma in '65. He quickly ordered various tests, including an ultrasonic scan.

Those indicated that something was wrong. The scan suggested that my spleen and liver were enlarged, and by then the gland in my neck was becoming quite noticeably swollen.

I was referred to the local hospital in Hemel Hempstead for minor surgery to allow a biopsy. After what seemed an interminable delay of three weeks, it was confirmed. I had another form of cancer, known as Non-Hodgkins Lymphoma and referred to as 'NHL' by the doctors. But not to worry, I was told! I would be put in the competent hands of a consultant oncologist (cancer specialist) at Mount Vernon Hospital, Hillingdon, and in due course treatment would be prescribed.

More tests followed at Mount Vernon, including bone-marrow examination, a CT scan, X-ray examinations, and blood tests. My consultant appeared not to be in too much of a rush. Being aware of my condition, and monitoring it a couple of times each week, gave her time and space to determine exactly the strain and extent of the lymphoma. I understand there are two main categories of lymphoma. There is a fast-developing type which, if caught early enough, can be treated with reasonable expectation of cure or lengthy remission. And there is a slow-developing type which is not ultimately curable but which can in many cases be kept in check for a considerable number of years.

It transpired that I had the former type, and that was

graphically impressed upon me by the rapid swelling of
more and more glands in my neck and shoulders. It got to
the place that from the tip of my chin, round the right side
of my face to the centre of my neck at the back, the swelling was extensive and becoming more and more uncomfortable. My right ear was being pushed upwards by the
swelling and to look in the mirror was rather disconcerting.
But still I was reassured that there was no reason to panic.
It was more important to know precisely what we were
dealing with.

Then one night, after I had noticed that the swelling
was moving inwards into my throat as well, I suddenly
woke from my sleep gasping for breath. My throat had momentarily closed because of the extent of the swelling, and
it felt as though I was going to suffocate. You can imagine I
hardly slept any more that night! Instead, I sat up against
my pillows trying to make sure I could breathe.

When we called the hospital early that April Thursday
morning, they told me to come in straight away. A further
examination indicated that treatment must begin immediately in order to control the rapid swelling and to make sure
my throat did not close altogether. That very day I began a
course of ten days of radiotherapy to the neck, reinforced by
steroid tablets. It controlled and reduced the swelling very
rapidly. In fact, by the Monday my neck was almost back to
normal.

A month later I was started on a six-month chemotherapy course; but, if I may, I should like to return in a
later chapter to the whole matter of radiotherapy and
chemotherapy treatments, and what it is like trying to cope
with them.

Once again I was supported by an ocean of prayer support, love and concern from family, friends, colleagues in
ministry and acquaintances from many parts of the world.
Just as in 1965, it proved an immense encouragement and
reinforcement to my own faith. And once again the Lord

blessed me with a deep sense of peace and inner strength. More of that later.

I related the medical aspects of my 1988 experience to Andrew. That brought me more or less up to date. I had returned to work in January 1989 and had been in good health ever since. Each check-up at out-patients and each CT scan had indicated the NHL had gone. I enjoyed physical strength and to all intents and purposes no one would have known that I had been ill.

Andrew took all that in. He then carried out a physical examination of my abdomen. Skilled hands detected spots where my body temperature was higher (indicating infection), places where the intestine was firmer than normal, and where it had formed a 'mass' near to the location of the appendix and upwards towards my liver.

He was calm and reassuring, but he counselled that I really should get into an accident and emergency wing of a hospital without delay. It seemed likely that I had appendicitis and that in defence my body had formed a 'mass' to prevent the spread of infection following a suspected rupture of the appendix itself. With my medical history, however, that was not the only possibility and it would be advisable to report into a hospital that day. . . .

We considered whether to travel to Bangor — the town with the nearest hospital to Aberdaron with casualty facilities — or whether it might be more convenient to return to Nottingham. That would certainly make it simpler for Sheila to cope with visiting, as long as the journey was sensible to undertake in the circumstances.

I talked it over with Sheila, and we opted to return to Nottingham. At about 7pm that evening we started homeward, and by a little after midnight I was reporting to 'Accident and Emergency' at the Queen's Medical Centre (QMC), Nottingham's University Hospital.

Blessed are your eyes because they see!

I must digress and tell you the story of Richard.

Back in April 1988, when I had been admitted to Mount Vernon Hospital when my throat had closed during the night, I was placed in Ward 1A. It had four bays, each with eight beds. All the patients on that ward were oncology (cancer) patients, as far as I knew.

My bed was on the near right as you entered the bay, and Richard arrived the next day — Friday — and was put into the bed on the far left, diagonally opposite me so to speak.

He was very, very ill. He was a deathly white, too weak to move his body or his limbs; and if it is not too unkind a thing to say, he looked rather like one of those tragic figures you see in pictures of famine-stricken East Africa — just skin and bone. He had a bed with a special air mattress that was programmed constantly to inflate and deflate to make the patient as comfortable as possible and to avoid the possibility of bed sores.

His arrival had a noticeable effect on the other patients. It was as though each man suddenly had a lock on his neck which prevented him from looking in Richard's direction. Perhaps it was too painful a thing to do, because each of us feared that one day soon we could also be that ill.

Through that Friday Richard hardly moved, except as the mechanized bed moved for him. During the Saturday, one of the nurses showed him a control pad on which he could press a selection of buttons and adjust the angle of the bed himself, thus raising his feet or his head. In the afternoon he managed to raise the head end of the mattress by that means, and thus had something of a view down the ward.

Somehow I felt that as a Christian pastor I ought to try to make some conversation with Richard, partly because no one else seemed able even to acknowledge him there, and partly because perhaps God might use me to bring him some encouragement.

But I had no idea of what to say or how to approach such a sick man. After all, you can hardly open with a comment like 'It's a lovely day isn't it!' I got off my bed with a prayer that God would give me something sensible to say.

'I'm in for lymphoma, what are you in for?' was my opening gambit when I arrived at his side. It was a little weak, but I hoped it would provide some point on which we could talk for a while.

'That's what I'm in for', he replied. My heart sank. The first thought that entered my head was, 'This is me in a few weeks' time when the lymphoma really gets a hold.' But my faith recovered and I remarked, 'But I'm only a young fellow still, just 42.'

I suppose I said that because Richard looked as though he might be in his seventies.

'I'm 41,' he said. My heart sank again. That was my destiny! That was what I was going to face if the treatment did not work! I wanted to walk away, go back to my bed and feel sorry for myself, but somehow I couldn't let him down. I felt that the privilege of having peace with God myself should in some way extend beyond me and offer peace to Richard, too.

I stayed my ground and we talked on. We got on to the subject of how we were diagnosed. I told him about the swollen gland in my neck and the sudden closure of my throat a couple of nights previously.

Richard told me he was Polish, had been married to an English girl but that the marriage had broken down. He had not seen his wife nor children for some years. He also told me that his lymphoma had not manifested itself in his neck but in his groin. He had gone to his GP and shown him the swelling in his groin, and the doctor had told him it was a hernia. Pain-killing tablets had been pre-scribed.

For some months that treatment had appeared to work. Then a second and a third swelling came up. The second time the GP had said, 'Well, now you have two hernias don't you!' It was not until Richard's testes swelled too that the GP thought that his original diagnosis might be in-correct. A visit to what was then his local hospital in Lancashire confirmed the lymphoma; but by then it was so established that treatment had proven ineffective.

The radiotherapy treatment I had at Mount Vernon worked so well that they let me go home on the following Monday. But I noticed that Richard had received no visitors at all; so I asked him if he had friends or family nearby.

It turned out that his mum lived at Aylesbury but could not manage the train into London and then back out to Mount Vernon, only to have to face it again on the return journey. She also had difficulty with the English language and had somehow got by with her Polish version of English; but tended to confine herself to places near her home where she knew folk and was known by them.

I asked Richard if he would like to see his mum, if per-haps I could manage to bring her into the hospital while I was coming in for radiotherapy as an outpatient. He gave me his mum's neighbour's telephone number and I agreed I would do my best to bring her with me later that week. I am so pleased that we did make contact and we did manage to bring her to see Richard on the Wednesday. He died on the Friday.

I relate Richard's story because so many times I have heard the prayer or offered the prayer myself on behalf of a sick person, that God would open the eyes of the physi-cians so that they might see rightly what was there. With all the best will in the world, sometimes a doctor misses the wood for the trees and makes a wrong diagnosis.

But, in a sense, I had felt that that prayer was a 'cop out', a kind of avoidance of a direct prayer that God would heal, just in case such a bold prayer failed. It was an easier prayer to make, simply to ask the Lord to 'open the eyes of the physician' or to 'guide the hands of the surgeon'. There was less risk.

Today I have a different view, and believe that one of the most valuable prayers we can make for the sick is that God will lead in the diagnosis, and make plainly visible to the doctor what he needs to recognize in order to make an accurate and early diagnosis.

I relate Richard's story because of the response of the doctor who received me at the Queen's Medical Centre, Nottingham, in July 1993.

Andrew had provided me with a covering letter to pass to the doctors at QMC, to which they did not appear to pay a great deal of attention. I suppose it is right that any examining doctor should begin without bias or influence, so as to arrive at his own conclusion.

A few X-rays and tests and a couple of hours later the doctor came to give me his assessment. In his view I did not have, nor had I had, appendicitis. He did not agree that there was any appendix mass. He said my intestine was very full of gas and that once that had been passed out of my system I would feel all right. He sent me home.

Less than thirty-six hours later my own GP had to have me re-admitted to the QMC because I was so ill. Within days, further tests and a biopsy confirmed that the NHL had returned — in my intestine. The consultant called it gastro-intestinal lymphoma. Apparently it had eaten through the wall of the intestine just below my liver, causing partly-digested foods, liquids and gases to escape into the peritoneum, causing the same effect almost as peritonitis

A 'mass' had indeed occurred — not an appendix mass as such, but Andrew had been correct. And today I thank God that He gave Andrew the skills and the perception; that He 'opened the eyes of the physician' and he recognized that something drastic had occurred.

To be taken three times a day before meals

I do not take my Bible with me into hospital.

For a start, my favourite Bible cost a lot of money and is very valuable to me. I use it for personal devotional reading, for study and sermon research, and for preaching from the pulpit. I do not want it to be damaged or lost in hospital.

Secondly, I like to take advantage of the Gideon Bible provided in each hospital locker, and I have a personal hope that if other patients see me take out the one from my locker, perhaps they will feel encouraged to take out theirs, too. It is not too old-fashioned a thing to do.

And it was when reading my Gideon Bible one day in the ward at the Queen's Medical Centre that I came across Psalm 116. I must have read it before, but suddenly it had great personal significance to me and I felt that God was giving me reassurance. This Psalm has become 'mine' ever since. Let me remind you of how it reads.

'I love the Lord, because he has heard
    my voice and my supplications.
Because he has inclined his ear to me,
Therefore I will call upon him as long as I live.
The pains of death encompassed me,
And the pangs of Sheol laid hold of me;
I found trouble and sorrow.
Then I called upon the name of the Lord:
"O Lord, I implore you,
    deliver my soul!"
Gracious is the Lord, and righteous;
Yes, our God is merciful.

The Lord preserves the simple;
I was brought low, and he saved me.
Return to your rest, O my soul,
For the Lord has dealt bountifully with you.
For you have delivered my soul from death,
My eyes from tears,
And my feet from falling.
I will walk before the Lord
In the land of the living.
I believed, therefore I spoke,
"I am greatly afflicted."
I said in my haste,
"All men are liars."
What shall I render to the Lord
For all his benefits towards me?
I will take up the cup of salvation,
And call upon the name of the Lord.
I will pay my vows to the Lord
Now in the presence of all his people.
Precious in the sight of the Lord
Is the death of his saints.
O Lord, truly I am your servant;
I am your servant,
    the son of your maidservant;
You have loosed my bonds.
I will offer to you the sacrifice of thanksgiving,
And will call upon the name of the Lord.
I will pay my vows to the Lord
Now in the presence of all his people,
In the courts of the Lord's house,
In the midst of you, O Jerusalem.'
Praise the Lord!
(NKJV) New King James Version.

I cannot explain, especially to a sceptic, why a Psalm written some 1,000 years before Christ and apparently read at random by (dare I claim) an intelligent and educated person living 2,000 years after Christ, should have the effect that my reading of Psalm 116 had. I cannot explain what happens in the heart or mind or soul of a human to make him think that God has in some way spoken directly and specifically to him. I just know from a number of personal experiences that from time to time it does definitely happen that way.

As I sat in my bed that moment, I knew deep in my being that that was an assurance from God. He had dealt bountifully with me and my troubled mind could rest. One day, in the presence of His people, I would have opportunity again to 'pay my vows to the Lord' by giving Him praise and honour for what He has done in my life. Perhaps it would be 'here and now' in this life, or perhaps it would be in the kingdom after Jesus' Second Coming had wiped away death and tears. One way or the other, the promise is certain and it brought me peace.

I tried to read that Psalm to Sheila when she came to visit me, but my heart and voice were full of tears. It was such a powerful promise and reassurance.

I had, by that time, been in hospital almost without a break from mid-July to mid-September 1993. I had been so ill that I did not eat any solid food for more than three weeks. I had suffered hiccuping-bouts two hours long. The surgeon had had to insert a drain into my right side to drain off the discharge from the fistula in my intestine. I had been kept hydrated by an intravenous drip, and the lack of protein had caused my legs and body to fill with fluid so that my legs were almost too heavy for me to lift.

The doctors encouraged me to try to eat again. I started off on liquid foods and then moved to a high-protein diet; but the part of my intestine near my right kidney was constantly in pain from the lymphoma. My stomach suffered the most painful cramps. Facing any food at all was a trial.

And in the midst of all that, God heard my cry for help

and it was He who led me to Psalm 116. Of that I have no doubt.

I told the doctors the next day that I wanted to go home. They looked at me almost with disdain; but we knew one another well by then and they understood my longing to get into my own bed, eat my wife's cooking, and be where I felt comfortable. Mark, the registrar, gently said that they wanted to see me much more mobile and independent with a significant advance in my general wellbeing before I could expect to go home.

It was a Friday and I decided the fight was on. That day I got off the bed and had Sheila act like a human Zimmer frame as I struggled to walk up and down the ward corridor. The first time I could manage only one length before I was totally exhausted. Later, when my mum took over from Sheila while she went to work, Mum became my human Zimmer, and I did two lengths. Later, I managed three.

The next day Mum escorted me round the complete block of that floor of the hospital. I had to hold on to her shoulder to steady myself; but I was going to win that fight and get discharged for home. By Sunday I did three complete laps of that block of the hospital unaided, Mum or Sheila walking a stride ahead of me just in case I needed an 'emergency landing'.

On the Monday my consultant did his rounds with his entourage of registrar and senior and junior house doctors. Moments before they started their rounds, Sheila and I were going to tackle another lap of the block. As I passed the huddle of doctors, I interrupted them and asked Mark whether I had time to walk round the block before they reached my bed. He looked surprised that I was even trying it, but said with a smile on his face, 'That depends on how long it takes you to get round.' I was back in a new lap record time!

'Can I go home today?' I asked my consultant as he

came to my bed. I was deliberately sitting in the chair beside my bed, and as he arrived I stood up, sat on my bed and swung my legs up as if it was no bother at all; then lay down ready for his examination of my abdomen.

As he deftly examined me, he consulted with Mark and the others on the team, who gave him a smiling nod, then he looked back at me. 'I think you can go home Wednesday *if* you have continued with this progress,' he said.

As they left me, Mark looked back at me shaking his head in disbelief. 'I cannot believe the progress you have made. I have never seen anyone recover so dramatically from the level of sickness you reached.'

'Well, you know, I do have a strong faith and I believe that makes the difference.' I knew that God was with me because He had given me peace, and with it He gave me determination and stamina to fight and not cave in.

If you are sick or have a friend or relative who is sick, please do take this prescription three times a day before meals. Close your eyes and ask God to take the burden from your heart, then open your eyes and give Him a chance to give you peace by reading something from the Bible. A Psalm or something from the Gospel of Mark will be a good starting point.

Pennies from heaven?

'I hope you get well soon. Thank you for visiting us at the school. Some people forgot what you looked like, but Mrs. Marriot said you were a teddy-like person. We are thinking of you.' Elliott.

Elliott is a pupil at a Christian school in Birmingham of which I am chairman of the board, and from which every pupil wrote a get-well-soon letter to me in November 1993.

These letters, and the scores of letters and cards that have come to Sheila and me from family, friends, colleagues and church members are truly pennies from heaven — gifts of God's love which bring encouragement and hope. The inspiration that they have been is like an ocean of buoyant water, supporting us and enabling us to cope.

Benjamin from the same school wrote:

'I like you because you came to my school. And we like you because you gave us some sweets and you told a story and you went in my class.'

And then Ayroza wrote:

'I am sorry that you are very ill but God will be with you. God is going to bless you and will make you better. I am praying for you and hoping you get better so much so that you can come back to our school.'

And this one came from Oeiisha:

'I hope you get well soon. I'm praying for you and I'm thinking of you. I hope you can come back one day when you are well.'

We have about ten cards and letters signed by each member of the sending church, and these words came from the prayer group which meets every week in a church in Handsworth:

'Prayer changes things. They who pray shall mount up as on eagle's wings. We are making supplications and prayers on

your behalf to our High Priest, the Lord and Saviour Jesus Christ. We know He will do for you what He sees best.'

Other cards have come from individuals, quoting texts of scripture or verses of poetry, like this one from a friend named Paul:

'The righteous cry, and the Lord heareth, and delivereth them out of all their troubles.' (Psalm 34:17.)

'The Lord will strengthen him upon the bed of languishing: thou wilt make all his bed in his sickness.' (Psalm 41:3.)

> *'More things are wrought by prayer*
> *Than this world dreams of, wherefore let thy voice*
> *Rise like a fountain for me day and night.*
> *For what are men better than sheep or goats*
> *That nourish a blind life within the brain*
> *If, knowing God, they lift not hands of prayer*
> *Both for themselves and those that call them friend?*
> *For so the whole round earth is every way*
> *Bound by gold chains about the feet of God.'*
>   Alfred, Lord Tennyson.

And this from Claudette and Lloyd:

> *'I'd gather roses without thorns, Lord,*
> *A bright and fragrant, beautiful bouquet*
> *To decorate my world with pretty pleasures —*
> *The brambles and the briars, I'll throw away.*
> *But you say I must pluck thorns as well, Lord,*
> *Though they'll pierce my heart and sting my soul;*
> *You say that pain's a part of peace, you tell me*
> *That breaking is a part of being whole . . .*
>
> *'You say that if I truly want to know you,*
> *I must count everything but Christ a loss;*
> *You ask me to exchange my will for yours, Lord,*
> *To trade contentment's kingdom for a cross.*
> *And so I come before you, weak but willing;*

> *I seek to walk your path, and not my own;*
> *I choose to share the crown of thorns you wore, Lord,*
> *Until I kneel before your royal throne.'*
>   B. J. Hoff

'*When life seems to hold more thorns than roses, may you remember that Jesus, who knows all about thorns, stands close beside you to see you through.*'

And then Heilene and Alvin wrote from Manchester:

'*Whenever you feel discouraged, remember Job and keep trusting and praying, even when the burden seems overwhelming. I pray these texts will comfort you — Isaiah 41:10, 13; Psalm 91 and Psalm 42:8. You and your family are in our thoughts and daily devotions. Please get well soon.*'

Young people have written to us, too. There was Jo, who wrote:

'*I just want to let you know that I'm thinking about you and praying for you and your family. I'd also like to thank you from the bottom of my heart for all the help and encouragement you've given me. It may not seem much to you, but you've helped me move mountains.*'

A 14-year-old simply wrote — '*Thinking and praying hard for your recovery.*' And Alison and Dave wrote:

'*I know you probably won't feel like reading a book, so I will try to keep it short. . . . I just wanted to let you know my prayers are for you and the family. I hope you are feeling better. You have given spiritual medicine to many youth and I know that many are praying that you will continue to minister to their needs.*'

Then we had a host of cards and letters from colleagues in ministry, including the following:

'*It must be a great disappointment to you both to find that once again you face sickness and uncertainty. There is so little to say which you do not already know because you have dealt with it before. But we just want you to know that we, along with many, many friends, feel for you and pray for you.*

'*This time round it must be hard to face. You've been through the treatment before — both of you — and it must be discouraging to think of going through it again. But with the help of God and doctors, you did it then, and it wasn't for nothing that God brought you through. "Let not your heart be discouraged."* '

Another letter came from a person I first met at one of my earliest summer camp duties in South Wales. She was then a camper, and today she is the wife of a minister. Together they make a fine team, and she wrote for both of them:

'*I just wanted to write and encourage you to hold on to God at this very difficult time . . .*

'*God is real; He does care, and He is better than fair; He's merciful, too. He is listening to your prayers, to Sheila's, to your sons', to ours, to the church family's — on your behalf. Whatever happens will be to God's glory even if it seems hard to us at the time; but whether you live or die, if you hold on to Jesus, He'll make sure you live forever.*

'*I expect you feel pretty rough at the moment, but just remind yourself of all the times when you have known God's intervention, have felt His presence. These will comfort you — and Sheila too. Remember that He's real all right and He loves you; He loves you; He loves you.*'

Then we received a letter from someone who graduated with me from Newbold College. Now married to a minister in the north of England, she wrote:

'*It has done my outlook on life good seeing the response of the members to your needs. Every service, especially the fellowships and prayer meetings, you and your family have been remembered.*

'*As you overcome the last large doses of treatment, you will be greatly relieved and we praise God for all the medical help you have received.*'

Finally, as a sample of letters from colleagues in

ministry, we received these lovely thoughts from friends living in Watford:

'*We have recently been doing a little study on the prayers of Paul and came across J. B. Phillips' translation of Colossians 1:11, 12 yesterday and would like to share it with you:*

'*"We pray that you will be strengthened from God's boundless resources, so that you will find yourselves able to pass through any experience and endure it with joy. You will even be able to thank God in the midst of pain and distress because you are privileged to share the lot of those who are living in the light."*

'*That's a tall order, but we are sure that as you look back over your lives and see the way God has led and blessed in the past, you will be convinced that He can give you all the strength you need just now.*'

And I cannot close this chapter without examples from two other groups of letters and greetings we have received. There were a number who recognized that Sheila has been going through a trial every bit as testing and exhausting as my own. I have appreciated so much the fact that some took the time to write directly and personally to her.

For example, Cynthia wrote:

'*I just wanted you to know that here at the office, as well as in our personal prayers, we are praying for you, as well as for Mike and the boys.*

'*We are asking that God will give you all the strengths you need to carry you through each day.*'

And this from Rosemary:

'*Just a few lines to let you know that we have not forgotten YOU. We often think just of YOU and remember you in our prayers just as we pray for Mike.*'

Or this from Alison:

'*I was sorry to hear about Mike. It must be difficult for you to go through it all again and try to be strong for everyone else. My reason for writing was to tell you that we are thinking about YOU. You are all in our prayers daily.*'

And last but not least, may I share a portion of one letter from a colleague in ministry and his wife, who at that time were walking through the same cancer experience:

'We were so sorry to hear that your health problems are back, Mike. As you know, we are walking through our own valley at the moment, and we can truly understand what you must be feeling just now. My husband's writing hand is not as strong as it used to be, but he has dictated the following message for you:

' "We know you must have a very strong faith, because you have bounced back so valiantly in the past. I am confident that the Lord will restore you again, and we are praying for you and asking Him to bless you."

'His condition continues to deteriorate and we know that without the Lord's special healing, he will not make it.

'In the post this morning a friend sent us these wonderful words which have always been a favourite of mine, only I'd never thought to apply it to this particular situation. But we found it immensely comforting and hope you will, too.

' "I said to the man who stood at the gate of the year: Give me a light that I may tread safely into the unknown. And he replied: Go out into the darkness and put your hand into the hand of God. That shall be better than a light and safer than a known way." '

And now I must explain why I have taken a whole chapter, just sharing letters, cards and messages made personally to me or to Sheila. It was not to give the impression that I am a very popular bloke! It was to convey a message that I think is an important one for those who are suffering illness which is possibly terminal, and for those spouses and family who are brought into anguish and pain because they fear that they may soon lose one they love.

The message is this: Do *please* write, telephone, visit as you are able. Sometimes it is hard for *us* (especially the inhibited English) to say in words the deep feelings of our hearts. We want to say something, but will we say it properly? Will it come over as we mean it? Will it sound too 'mushy' or be embarrassing?

Having 'been there' three times now, I believe that I want to hear what people want from their hearts to say to me, while I am here to hear them. There have been numerous occasions when it seems God timed a letter or card from a friend, just when I needed it most. It has meant so much to me. It has lifted my spirits, given me strength to fight on. Sometimes it has brought tears to my eyes and I have sobbed my heart out for five minutes. But it has brought me blessing.

You have a ministry which, however humble you may feel it to be, can be used by God. So write a notelet or send a card — not just once but every few weeks. Fill it, not with platitudes but with those meaningful words which come from your own soul. And thereby you will bring strength and appreciation that can never be measured.

Don't just sit there, say something!

The view from the lounge in Roundelwood is inspiring. Set on the side of a hill above the central Scotland town of Crieff, it is sufficiently elevated to look without obstruction over the town to the forests and mountains beyond.

In winter, the trees hang laden with snow, Christmas-card style. In summer, all manner of rich green tints couch the houses and farms in a verdure which highlights the maturing crops and forestry and seeks to conceal the impress of mankind.

We were there at hay-making season in 1989. From our supper-table vantage point, we talked together, watching tractors across the vale silently cutting pale swathes among the rich grass, as evening motorists converged and departed town.

Roundelwood is reassuring. A home-from-home as it were, combining, in an unique way, residential care for the elderly with a modern health centre, equipped with gymnasium, pool, physiotherapy, hydrotherapy and recreational therapy, facilities to which business couples resort from all over the UK.

Sheila and I were at Roundelwood at the invitation of administrator Martin Bell. A long-time friend from our days together at Newbold College, Martin had visualized providing a retreat week at the health centre for cancer patients and spouses. Local health authorities had responded by sponsoring a number of couples to occupy the comfortably-appointed twin bedrooms.

The 'team' for the week consisted of Martin — who would oversee the whole programme and provide talks on how to minimize the harrowing effects of the disease and treatments by diet and life-style; Terry — a retired GP who would provide confidential counsel and talks to the group on the medical aspects of the disease; Roundelwood's resident staff who run the normal health programme; and Sheila and me. My role was to provide a pastoral element, bearing in mind my training as a minister and my personal experience as a cancer patient.

To put that special week chronologically into my experience, remember that 1988 had been the year I was diagnosed as having Non-Hodgkins Lymphoma and in which I had had radiotherapy and six months of chemotherapy. I had returned to work on 2 January 1989, and by then had arrived at May/June of that year.

We shared the supper-table that evening with Robbie and Joan (not their real names); and to a casual observer one would have thought the scene idyllic. Comfortable surroundings, excellent food, pleasant company, and a view that instilled tranquillity. Yet all was not what it seemed.

Joan was the cancer patient. She was terminally ill. A lovely lady with a warm Dundee accent, she spoke softly at table, yet with a tear in her voice.

Robbie was a strapping big chap, or at least he had been in his day. By then retired, he absolutely adored his wife. He spoke with the staccato punctuation of a Glaswegian. He had a heart of gold, but his heart was breaking. There were tears in his voice, too; but they were concealed by an endless stream of jokes and one-liners.

That afternoon I had presented a talk in which I sought to communicate our experience — Sheila's and mine — as we learned of my cancer in 1988, as we were told of the extent of the invasion by the disease, the anticipated treatment, and the prognosis.

I had shared with the folk the way we had tried to come to terms with it, given that we had a family of teenage sons who were also trying to cope with such traumatic news. I had spoken about how we, as a couple, had confronted the possibility of death, what that might mean to Sheila and the boys, what it meant to me. We had talked of life insurance, and protection of the home.

I had told them I was not afraid of being dead, because as a Christian I had faith in a God who would one day raise me from the grave, and that He had made a cast-iron promise in Scripture which removed all fear of death itself. But I had to admit I was afraid of the process of dying, the pain and suffering that I might physically have to endure.

I explained that we each had the same options; to bottle these things up inside, or to talk about them as frankly and gently as we could. We could deny or we could accept cancer and all that it threatens. In our case, there had been moments when we could not talk; but had wanted only to pull down the blinds and retreat into our own shells.

But we had also had times when we could talk, and deliberately chose to talk together. Often that had been at bedtime, with lights off so that the pain of talking was not anguished by the sight of tears on cheeks or distress in the eyes.

My thesis for the afternoon had been that the cancer victim, the spouse, the children, the parents, the grandparents, even the friends — each had an aching heart which sought relief by talking, even in the inhibited stereotypical British personality. It was hard to crack the ice and broach the subject, but to deny it and keep it bottled up would leave a grief beyond death which could not be healed.

I have seen too many families tip-toeing round the word 'cancer', afraid to open their hearts to one another. I have seen fellow patients who know full well they are dying from cancer declining to admit it, lest they distress their families.

Equally, I have watched the family saying nothing to their husband/father/son in case the mention of cancer should in some way hasten or make inevitable his passing.

And I know from personal experience of being ill with cancer, and from professional experience of talking with other cancer patients, that their greatest desire is to talk about it. It brings such relief to the soul, not to just sit there but to say something.

That had been my theme, and following a delightful gourmet supper that evening at Roundelwood, the tears in Joan's voice and the laughter-concealed tears in Robbie's voice belied the idyllic scene across the vale.

I interrupted his stream of jokes by putting my hand on his. 'Robbie, you love Joan so much, but there is something she needs which you are denying her. She wants you to talk about her illness together. She wants to talk about how you will manage when she is gone.'

Robbie burst into tears, the jokes finally overcome by grief. 'I cannot,' he cried. 'The only way I can handle this is to distract myself with jokes. All my life that is how I have coped.'

Joan's hand reached across the table and held his. 'But, Robbie, my heart is breaking. Please let us talk.' Tears cascaded down her face and his. I think that that night they talked and cried themselves to sleep. But they had provided a therapy for each other which would in time make the grief easier to bear.

You must have been there, too. You must have had an experience when a tragedy or bereavement had occurred to a friend. You wanted to say something, but you felt uncomfortable about it and were worried about quite what to say and how it would be received. All I can say is that from personal experience as a cancer victim, the people I have appreciated most are those who have broken through that reticence and opened their hearts or encouraged me to open mine.

And I believe that as a cancer patient or the spouse of a cancer patient, one also has a ministry to provide to one's friends and relatives to help them over this reticence.

For example, back in 1988 as word spread round the office that I had cancer, I sensed that some secretaries were in the position in which they wanted to say something but did not know how to start or whether just to keep silent. In spite of a very good 'family feeling' in the church headquarters' office, I sensed that when Sheila popped in to see me there, some felt so distressed and uncomfortable they would avoid us rather than meet us.

So Sheila and I discussed it together and we agreed that she would pop into the offices of one or two and take the initiative by talking with them. Not just casual talk about the weather, but specific talk about how she was feeling and how she and the boys were coping.

We noticed that people relaxed after that, and one or two actually said to me they had so wanted to say something and that Sheila's talk had helped.

Now I know that it is not necessarily in vogue to talk about things 'up front'. I know that in some cases hospital consultants decide not to tell the patients they have cancer for fear this will cause them to 'give up'. Perhaps they decide not to tell the relatives either — who knows?

But I also know from observation and from experience that the folk who cope best are those who manage to talk about it. If this book achieves nothing else, I hope at least it will encourage someone somewhere to share the burden of his heart with his loved one while it is still possible to do so.

Before I close this chapter, let me say a word about feelings of guilt.

It is an odd thing, but when I survived the NHL in 1988, I felt guilty in the company of widows of friends who had died from cancer that same year. I have spoken with a colleague whose grand-daughter is surviving leukaemia and chemotherapy, who feels guilty in the presence of friends whose child or grand-child has died from the same disease.

I suppose this is a somewhat natural reaction, because we do not feel we have an adequate explanation of why our loved one should survive when another perishes. Are we somehow better or more worthy in God's sight? Why didn't God let their relative survive too? We have no satisfactory answers.

But may I suggest the resolution lies in the same counsel — go and talk with that person and address the problem. Tell her, 'I almost feel guilty that I am here and your husband is not. I cannot explain why it should have happened this way round, and I just hope my being here does not make you feel resentment or cause your grief to be multiplied.' Talking about it, I hope, will be a mutual therapy.

John Bunyan's puddle

I like John Bunyan. He is one of my favourite Christian characters because there are a number of ways in which I feel ordinary Christians like me can identify with him. For a start, in my case he was what you might call a 'near neighbour'.

In 1963 my family had moved from Norwich to RAF Cardington, just south of Bedford. Dad was employed as a civilian with the RAF, and when his station at Horsham St. Faith closed, he was given the option of transferring to RAF Henlow, or of leaving the service. He opted for the transfer, and the nearest MOD housing they could provide to Henlow was at Cardington.

A mile or two west of our new home nestled the village of Elstow, John Bunyan's village. If you struck out across the footpaths and fields from our house, you could find a plaque in the corner of a field which said that there once stood a cottage in which his parents had lived, and in which Bunyan was born and spent his childhood. Carry on a bit farther and you will reach Elstow itself, and you will notice a number of half-timbered houses and buildings such as the Moot Hall and the parish church, which were all there in Bunyan's day.

Unfortunately, today no cottage remains in which Bunyan lived. Even the one to which he moved later in life has crumbled away. I remember when the authorities made the decision that it was 'too far gone' to salvage.

Then there was his rough-and-ready appearance and character that appealed to me. He had a mop of red hair and a chunky build befitting his itinerant blacksmith trade. He loved life, and especially loved the village life where the youth would meet on the village green of an evening and play their favourite games, including tip-cat. He had a love and a genius for music and for making musical instruments; and one of his best-loved activities was to join in the bell ringing at the church.

Bunyan had a wonderful imagination as any reading of his works will testify, especially *Pilgrim's Progress*. This imagination sometimes led him into mischief. Years later when he was imprisoned, he had his favourite chair brought to his cell, from which he carefully removed one of the dowels in the back. He carved it into a flute, and would while away his time playing it until he heard the warden coming round. Then he would quickly conceal it back in the chair.

The warden finally began to crack, and told Bunyan he thought the hobgoblins were after him. He could hear a flute being played, but he knew no one down there who had a flute. From that experience Bunyan wrote his hymn, 'He Who Would Valiant Be' — the original words of which have a reference to not fearing foul fiends or hobgoblins.

But poor John was haunted by what have been called 'religious terrors', nightmares which would wake him even as a young child, in which God was pursuing him to punish him for his sin. As a child he had a picture of God as some awful tyrant who was out to consume every sinner, and he was one of the worst. That had been indelibly burned into his thinking by the attitude of the parish vicar who held the belief that enjoyment of any pleasure such as tip-cat on the village green indicated total depravity. 'God will get you one day,' he had said into John's ear many a time.

As a young adult, John's search for peace with God led him to extensive Bible reading. He was convinced he was too bad for God ever to accept him, and at one stage he stopped going to the bell-tower because as he looked up at the huge castings pealing out their notes, he thought, 'That is how God will get me. He will drop one of those bells on me and crush me to death.'

One day he came across the verse in Hebrews 11:6: 'But without faith it is impossible to please him, for he who comes to God must believe that he is, and that he is a rewarder of those who diligently seek him.' (NKJV.)

Some time later John also came across the verse in Matthew 17:20: 'So Jesus said to them, "Because of your unbelief; for assuredly, I say to you, if you have faith as a mustard seed, you will say to this mountain, 'Move from here to there,' and it will move; and nothing will be impossible for you."' (NKJV.)

Those two verses began to jangle together in John's mind. 'Without faith', he mused, 'I cannot please God. If I have faith even as insignificant as a mustard seed, I can tell a mountain to move, and it will. Here, surely, is an acid test! I can find out whether I, John Bunyan, can satisfy God by testing whether I have even that little faith.'

If you know Bedfordshire, you know there are no mountains there. But John was not to be defeated; he would test his faith on a puddle. One day as he walked the track towards the village, he commanded a puddle to be moved. It didn't budge. John was shattered. If mountains take mustard seeds, surely puddles only take grains of sand; and apparently he did not even have that tiny amount. Was there no hope for him to please God?

You may smile at such naïvety, but when it comes to prayer for the sick, I feel that a great many Christians do virtually the same thing as John did. Let me explain.

Scripture contains what appear to be very unequivocal rock-solid promises, which seem to say that a believing Christian has only to ask and the request will be granted. For example, one verse that reads very much like that which John Bunyan found in Matthew 17:20, is Matthew 21:21: 'So Jesus answered and said to them, "Assuredly, I say to you, if you have faith and do not doubt, you will not only do what was done to the fig tree, but also if you say to this mountain, 'Be removed and be cast into the sea,' it will be done. And all things, whatever you ask in prayer, believing, you will receive."' (NKJV.)

Or this from James 5:14, 15: 'Is anyone among you sick?

Let him call for the elders of the church, and let them pray over him, anointing him with oil in the name of the Lord. And the prayer of faith will save the sick, and the Lord will raise him up. And if he has committed sins, he will be forgiven.' (NKJV.)

Many Christians pray for their sick loved ones. They rightly take these two verses to be a mandate to approach God boldly and ask Him to heal. Many are healed. You could fill a book with illustrations of answered prayer. But many are not. So how do you resolve this failure in the face of such unequivocal promises?

Well, normally we resort to the final clause of Jesus' words in Matthew 21:22 — '*believing*, you will receive.' And rather like John Bunyan and his puddle, we conclude that clearly we did not have enough faith. If we had had sufficient faith we could have gained the answer we sought, but obviously we could not quite tip the scales in our favour and convince God we believed. God's promise must be sure — the fault lies in our lack of faith.

But to fall into this trap denies the very reason Jesus spoke as He did. It is not a matter of building up enough faith finally to tip the scales. It is not a matter of volume nor quantity of faith. And you could ask for no other more forceful proof of that than from Jesus' own Gethsemane experience when He prayed, 'Take this cup from me.'

The specific request Jesus made was that He not partake of the cup of the wrath of God. If He could choose, He would not wish to endure the cross, and even less to be separated from His Father by taking upon Himself the guilt of humanity's sin. The thought of such separation was breaking His heart.

No one would suggest Jesus lacked faith in His Father to grant Him that request. So it was not a matter of the degree or volume of His faith that caused His request to be denied.

But Jesus had also uttered in His prayer, 'Take this cup from me, *yet not my will, but your will be done.*'

We must take into consideration other verses of Scripture on the subject of prayer. We cannot just claim Matthew 21:21 or James 5:15 in isolation from other verses, and it is always important to make certain that we incorporate everything the Bible teaches on any one point before drawing conclusions.

So we must balance these apparently unequivocal promises with the caution of a passage such as 1 John 5:13-15: 'These things have I written to you who believe in the name of the Son of God, that you may know that you have eternal life, and that you may continue to believe in the name of the Son of God. Now this is the confidence that we have in him, that if we ask anything according to his will, he hears us. And if we know that he hears us, whatever we ask, we know that we have the petitions that we have asked of him.' (NKJV.)

In other words, if we make a request that is not His will to grant, no amount of faith will effect a granting of that petition. Our prayers are answered positively if we pray something in accordance with His will.

This is why I prefer the translation 'trust' rather than 'faith'. Try reading Hebrews 11 and substituting 'By faith' with the words 'Because . . . trusted God, he . . . '.

Thus: 'Because Abraham trusted God, he obeyed God when he was called to go out . . . .'

I would like to think that we trust God, no matter what. I do not have to summon up enough quantity of faith to persuade Him to answer me. And surely the whole point of Jesus' mustard seed illustration is to show that quantity does not come into it.

Trust God, and He will see to it that your best good always prevails. That might be different from the way you pictured it. It may mean a loved one dies. But trust God. He is in control. As one writer put it: God 'never leads them otherwise than they would choose to be led if they could see the end from the beginning, and discern the glory of the purpose that they are fulfilling.'

The prayer of submission

Before I return to my own confrontation with cancer, let's explore this concept of the 'prayer of submission', which is an apt name for the prayer Jesus modelled in Gethsemane and for that approach to prayer that the Apostle John encouraged us to practise in 1 John 5. To do this we need to recall three Old Testament experiences of the people of Israel.

For me these three episodes say something about the kind of attitude I must have when I approach God in prayer. For example, I must be aware that perhaps I come with my own agenda which God must bless because I know what is best! I must be aware, too, that perhaps I come promising to live and do exactly as God wants me to do — whether His commands are comfortable or not — so long as they fit my plans! And I must be aware that sometimes I may come with some claim to merit in God's eye which is phoney because I have none, even if I manage to fulfil all His commands. Let me show you this from Scripture.

Just as I like John Bunyan, I also like Ezekiel. I think he is my favourite Old Testament character. I identify with him because I have spent twenty-five years in ministry, and have come to the conclusion that people have not changed that much from his time to mine.

I can picture Ezekiel, a young man in his mid-twenties, being rounded up by Nebuchadnezzar's army and herded into a long train of migrants. He had to cover on foot the hundreds of miles north and then east to Babylon, which corresponds largely to what we now know as Iraq.

And rather like those Kurdish and Marsh Arab refugees we see on our TV screens, Ezekiel and tens of thousands of other Israelites were left to fend for themselves in shanty towns of mud huts. Not for them the luxury of the royal household afforded to the Jewish aristocracy, including Daniel. Their lot was to eke out a survival-living as best they could. Fortunately, the land was fertile and they could grow much of their food.

Ezekiel's dream since childhood had been entry into the priesthood. He was a Levite, and many a time he had pictured himself serving in the temple at Jerusalem or serving the people of his village back home. All that was gone. For one thing, he was a hostage with little chance of returning to Israel, and, for another, Nebuchadnezzar had razed the temple in Jerusalem to the ground.

But God had other plans. One day, as Ezekiel sought peace and a tranquil place of prayer by one of the many irrigation canals in Babylonia, God came to him in vision and told him he was to have a ministry after all — the ministry of being a prophet, a spokesperson for God to the captive people of Israel.

Ezekiel's task would be tough, God told him, because the Israelites were still a stubborn and hard-headed people who refused to acknowledge they had gone astray from God. But not to worry, the stubbornness of the people was not to be Ezekiel's concern. His concern was to be a faithful prophet so that at the end of the day the people would know that there had been a prophet among them.

But then, as if to complicate Ezekiel's role even more, God told him: 'I want you to be My spokesman, but I am going to strike you dumb. You will only be able to talk when I release your tongue.' But again, not to worry because God had in mind a series of enacted parables which Ezekiel would perform outside his own mud hut.

These would include building a sand-castle and lying out beside it day after day for more than a year. He would have to shave all his hair and beard off, burning one-third, chopping one-third with his knife, and throwing the remaining one-third into the wind. He would have to break a hole through the wall of his own mud hut to signify the way Zedekiah — king of those few Jews who remained in Judah — would break out of the city of Jerusalem at night in an effort to evade the besieging King Nebuchadnezzar.

It wasn't long before the people began to recognize that Ezekiel was not suffering from sun stroke, but that he appeared to be a messenger of God. They recognized that the sand-castle was intended to represent Jerusalem; that Ezekiel lying facing away from the 'Jerusalem' sand-castle was looking towards the northern kingdom of Israel, and that lying facing towards the 'Jerusalem' sand-castle he was facing the southern kingdom of Judah — he was representing something that would happen to each sister kingdom of the descendants of Abraham.

They caught on that the breaking through Ezekiel's mud hut represented Zedekiah's abortive attempt to flee, because by then they had heard for themselves that Nebuchadnezzar had captured Zedekiah, put his eyes out and led him like an animal captive to Babylon.

The people recognized that Ezekiel had a special ministry to the point that they sent a delegation of elders to his home to ask him to pray for God's guidance on their behalf. On the face of it, that was a wonderful reverse for Israel, and though their specific enquiry is not spelled out, it appears at first glance to have been a genuine enquiry, because they wanted to be sure they were doing what God wanted them to be doing.

But God's response is startling. He says, 'I will not be enquired of by you!' Then follows a catalogue of the times God had been on the brink of abandoning Abraham's descendants. Time and again, He says, 'I was ready to call it quits with this people, but every time I stayed loyal to My covenant with Abraham because it is contrary to My character to do otherwise.'

The reason for this outburst is perhaps explained later in the chapter, in a verse which may explain their original enquiry. 'What you have in your mind will never be, when you say, "We will be like the Gentiles, like the families in other countries, serving wood and stone." '

I imagine what happened was as follows. Israel worshipped an invisible God, Yahweh, the God of Creation, who had explicitly told them they must not make graven images to represent Him. Then Israel found themselves hostages in Babylon, and the Babylonians made such a thing about parading images of their god Bel around the city that it made the God of Israel look rather weak. After all, it was Israel that was captive! Where was this invisible God they prayed to? Perhaps, the Babylonians teased them, their God was not as great as Bel.

So I imagine the elders coming to ask Ezekiel to pray on their behalf; 'Will it be all right in these circumstances to make an image.' Israel would know it did not really represent or contain God, but it would give substance to their religion. It would help them defend themselves against the jibes of the Babylonians.

On the face of it, it was a prayer of submission. But God exposed it for what it was. They were asking Him to turn a blind eye to something upon which He had insisted from the word go — NO graven images! They were not submissive at all. Not one bit. They just wanted God to bless their plans, even though they knew they would be anathema to Him. Their apparent prayer to be sure they were doing what God wanted them to be doing was nothing of the sort! You can read all about it in Ezekiel 20.

While Ezekiel was a young man beginning his ministry in Babylon, Jeremiah was an old man concluding his in Jerusalem. And not very long after the Ezekiel story, Jeremiah had a very similar approach from those Jews who had been left in Jerusalem. Nebuchadnezzar had taken Zedekiah by that time, and had left an administrator named Gedaliah to control civil affairs.

The Jews despised Gedaliah and looked upon him as a

quisling who had betrayed the interests and integrity of Israel in order to save his own skin. But they had a cunning plan. They would murder him, thereby giving him the end he deserved and simultaneously thumbing their noses at Nebuchadnezzar. But no sooner had the knives been withdrawn from the corpse than they realized their folly.

That would prove nothing to Nebuchadnezzar, except that they were inviting him to come back and wipe them all off the face of the earth. So they went to Jeremiah (see Chapter 42) and again, on the face of it, requested the most wonderful prayer of submission. They wanted to be sure they were doing what God wanted them to be doing.

'Please ask God what He wants us to do,' they begged, 'and whatever His answer, we will live by it.' So Jeremiah took the prayer and ten days later (note that God does not always answer prayer instantly) back came the reply.

The people had surmised they had two options. They could stay where they were in Israel and wait for Nebuchadnezzar's wrath, or they could flee to Egypt where they would be beyond his reach. But God's answer exposed the weakness of their prayer and the falseness of their purpose.

He told them in effect, 'All I ever wanted you to do was trust Me. Now if you will trust Me and stay put in Israel, I will protect you. You have nothing to fear of any human, even Nebuchadnezzar. But if you do not trust Me but run off to Egypt, the very things that you run from WILL reach you there and you will perish.'

Neither their prayer nor their commitment to accept whatever God indicated was submissive. God exposed the error of their judgement. And He shows us via the record of this event that prayer can be flawed if we already have only one answer that we will accept and we refuse any other possibility as coming from God.

About seventy years later the captivity was over, and people started returning to Israel. However, the majority stayed in what for them had become a very comfortable and prosperous life-style in Babylon, but several thousand *did* return and did rebuild Jerusalem.

And as you read Zechariah 7 you will find a third approach by the people of Israel to a prophet, so as to be sure they were doing what God wanted them to be doing.

The names Sherezer and Regem-Melech indicate that members of this delegation were Jews who still lived in Babylon, and who had been sent by fellow Jews who had remained there to seek God's counsel. On the face of it, once more, a commendable prayer of submission.

Their request was specific: 'Do we still need to keep up our fast days in the fifth and seventh months to commemorate the fall of Jerusalem and the mourning over the destruction of the Temple?' After all, Jerusalem was rebuilt, and the temple was on its way to completion. Surely they could stop this practice now, but they didn't want to offend God, so they asked first.

Once again God's reaction exposed their prayer for what it was. It was not a prayer of submission, because He had never asked them to keep those days of mourning in the first place. They were their own idea! But what God had asked was that they ' " 'Execute true justice, show mercy and compassion everyone to his brother. Do not oppress the widow or the fatherless, the alien or the poor. Let none of you plan evil in his heart against his brother.' " '

They had refused to heed, shrugged their shoulders, and stopped their ears to these expectations of God, and had substituted 'good deeds' of their own which God had never specified. A prayer is phoney when we come claiming 'brownie points' for human ideas but turn a deaf ear to the commands of God.

A prayer must always be truly a prayer of submission, in which we admit and acknowledge our faults and flaws, our hidden agendas, and our total need of God, with the request that though we ask for one thing, we wish to be truly and totally subject to His wisdom and will. Daniel 9:3-19 demonstrates what is a real prayer of submission.

I wrote the following note on 26 September 1993. I do not know whether I was in hospital or at home at the time, nor do I remember what prompted me to write it. But I think it makes good sense, and hopefully is a good note on which to conclude this chapter.

'God has no illusions about us; no false hopes which cannot become real; no expectations beyond what He Himself will enable us to achieve.

'Therefore God is not _disillusioned_ when we do fail or when we fall away from our relationship with Him.

'We may feel we have let Him down, that we are not doing enough for Him, or being sufficiently victorious.

'But not God! He knows our frame.'

With God, it is always a matter of recognizing what we are really like and admitting it to Him when we pray. As John says in 1 John 1:8, 9, if we deny our real condition then the only person we fool is ourselves — BUT we miss out on God's blessing. If, on the other hand, we recognize and admit to God our faults and failings, both known and unknown, He is absolutely trustworthy. He will both forgive our past and remedy our future.

In this context we can really ask God for our hearts' desires, concede happily that His will shall overrule ours, and know that the most wonderful things will happen to our lives and in our lives.

The service of anointing

'Oh, pastor, I am sorry to be calling you so early. It's Mary here. I am at the hospital. George was taken ill in the night. He had a stroke and is still in a coma. They've said he hasn't got long. Would you arrange for him to be anointed?' (Both names used are pseudonyms.)

The service of anointing is described in James 5:14, 15. Elders of the church were to pray over the sick believer, and he or she was to be anointed with oil in the Name of the Lord. It is a simple and usually private service, administered by a pastor or clergyman and some elders of the church — usually lay men of observable faith and commitment. Each, in turn, offers prayer for the sick person, and during the final prayer the subject is anointed on the forehead with olive oil.

It was sometime between 6.30 and 7am, and clearly Mary was distressed. It did not matter at all that it was on the early side. 'No problem,' I replied, 'I'll contact a couple of the elders to see if they are available; but I should think 11am will be the earliest we can get everything organized. Is that all right?' She understood, and we agreed that unless I came back to her by telephone, she could expect us there punctually.

I did have one or two problems, but I was not about to trouble her with them. My first was to contact two elders from our local churches to see if they were available. I called Brian first. He was a busy salesman with business appointments to keep, but he willingly had his office postpone the morning commitments so that he could be with us. Then I phoned Horace, a retired 'captain of industry' with many years' experience of management. But he was a busy retiree and he would have the farthest to travel. Yes, he would be delighted to be of service.

My next, and in some ways more daunting, problem was that I had never in my life observed an anointing service or been trained to lead one. I was a bit overwhelmed at the prospect of doing so at such a crucial time.

I would need some olive oil, and a container — perhaps a small glass bowl — from which to apply the oil to George's forehead when the moment came. Sheila quickly confirmed that we had both to hand; so at least I did not have to worry about rushing off to the shop!

Then, most importantly of all, and as I had suggested to Brian and Horace, too, I was very conscious of Jesus' explanation to the disciples who had failed to cast out a demon from a young boy. You can read the account in Matthew 17:14-21. (It is the same passage by which John Bunyan felt challenged to try to move his puddle!) When Jesus cast the demon out, the disciples asked why they had failed. Part of Jesus' response was: 'This kind does not go out except by prayer and fasting.'

To me, that meant that Brian, Horace and I must spend as much of the intervening time as possible in our own prayers. We did not wish for any impediment in our own lives, or in our approach to God on George's behalf, to hinder or prevent God's blessing.

I had about fifteen miles to travel to the hospital; so I left home in good time and in the event found myself with about twenty minutes to spare. So I stopped the car in a lay-by and spent some more time in prayer. I did not want my sin to obstruct God's blessing. I did not look upon an anointing as some kind of magic formula which would compel God to grant our request. I wanted to enter the hospital ward from a position of faith and confidence in that I knew how to pray and what to hope for.

As I said in an earlier chapter, I cannot explain — least of all to a sceptic — what takes place in these circumstances, but I was gradually aware of the peace of God, and I had a confidence as if God were saying to me, 'It's all right, Mike. You can ask Me for this because I am going to do it!'

George was in a small side ward, in which the other bed was unoccupied. That was good because we would neither intrude upon other patients nor be intruded upon once we started our service. Brian and Horace joined Mary and me as we agreed our 'order of service'. Mary wished to pray too, so we decided Brian would lead, since he was co-elder with George in the local church. Mary would then precede Horace, and I would conclude and do the anointing.

We read a passage of Scripture together as George lay between us, still in a deep coma. When I came to the point in my prayer at which I was to anoint him, I dipped my fingers into the oil and bathed his forehead with it, pronouncing the anointment in the Name of the Lord and asking God to reach into George's life again to heal and into Mary's life to bring her strength and courage.

When we left the ward, nothing appeared to have happened. George had not sat upright in bed. We could not call the nurse and tell her all was well and that Mary would be taking George home right then. But we all felt the closeness of God, and the kind of peace which He alone promises when we submit ourselves to His will. I promised Mary I would call back after lunch.

At about 2.30pm I walked into the ward again and found her with a broad smile on her face, and the nurse brushing past me said, 'Isn't it marvellous what a little prayer will do!'

But George looked precisely the same as when I had left; so at first I did not understand their elation. Mary soon told me. Over the lunch break her husband had woken up, had recognized her, and had even laughed at a joke. He had fallen asleep. He was no longer in a coma.

George explained to me later that he had felt as though he was in a deep sleep from which he could not awaken. He said he was trying to wake up but somehow could not break through that barrier. Then he had felt a burning, almost scorching sensation on his forehead, and following that he had gradually been able to stir himself.

God had answered our prayer in the way we had requested of Him. All that happened in either 1972 or 1973. Now, twenty years on, George is still alive and kicking. True, he never recovered much use of his left limbs, but I understand most weeks you will find Mary and George in church. Surely we can only praise God that He is faithful to His Word today as He was two thousand years ago when Jesus raised people to life and health.

In 1993 it was my turn to be the subject of an anointing service. I was more ill than I had ever been in my life, even considering the teratoma in 1965 and the lymphoma in 1988.

Lionel is a good friend who has provided a lifetime of ministry in the Gospel sense and in the medical sense. His years of service have taken him to mission work in Africa, as well as to the heart of the inner cities of England. He knows what it is like to have no choice but to depend upon God. He is a man of faith who believes that an anointing must never be regarded as some sort of 'last rites' when all else has failed, but rather should be a first or early step in the process of prayer for the sick so that patient, family and God may know who is going to be in control of the situation. An anointing is for surrender to God's will.

I asked Lionel if he would contact Patrick and Egerton and arrange for me to be anointed. Patrick is a friend and colleague in ministry, and was the pastor of my next nearest local church when I fell ill in 1988. He had supported me perhaps more than any one else during that time, often phoning me to see if I would care to get out for an hour or two, praying with me, and providing someone just to talk to about things. He is a man bold yet humble in his prayers.

Egerton is my close colleague in church administration. I first came to meet him and Cynthia when I was the pastor of churches near to Newbold College and he was a student. He was seconded to my supervision at a church in Reading. We now work together as first and second officers of the Conference, and this has confirmed in my experience that he is a man of dignity and calm faith. Those were the 'elders' I wished to be present for my anointing.

Sheila and my mum were present when we convened, and Patrick led us in some devotional thoughts from Scripture to remind us of the wonderful way in which Christ identifies with our physical pain as well as with our spiritual pain. Then he invited me to consider my own standing before God, whether I had sins yet unconfessed — secret sins of the heart of which none but God and I knew, sins of commission or omission, stemming from simply being a human, or sins which compromise a ministry in God's Name.

I am not proud of every aspect of my life. I know that I have offended God and offended my neighbour, perhaps even become a stumbling block to some so that they may never find it in themselves to seek God. But I also know that each offence of which I am aware has been taken to the Lord, sometimes with tears and anguish, and I know He has forgiven just as He promised.

We proceeded with the prayers, Sheila and Mum praying, too. Then as Patrick prayed, all three ministers anointed me — one to my forehead, another to my abdomen where the seat of the cancer was, another to my wrists and ankles. My whole body was as it were anointed with oil, the symbol of God's grace and power.

I did not leap off the bed miraculously. Patrick did not invite me to get off my bed and walk, or to go and report to the consultant to show that I was 'clean'. But I had a wonderful sense of peace because I knew that I had passed my case to God. He was going to be in control. He would see to it that a wrong diagnosis or prescription would be overruled. It was to be His decision whether I recovered or whether I lay down my arms and rested until Jesus returns.

And that is why I believe that the anointing service is probably the most under-used ministry we have available in Christianity. In twenty-five years of ministry this was only the second anointing in which I had been involved — and one of them was my own!

Why this reluctance to use such a wonderful ministry? I suspect it is for a number of reasons.

✻ Perhaps we view an anointing rather as we do the writing of a will — we are reluctant because somehow we feel that proceeding with it is going to hasten death.

✻ Perhaps we view it as a sort of Protestant 'last rites' which needs only to be asked for when it is inevitable the subject will die.

✻ Perhaps we view it as a last resort. When all the medical expertise we can benefit from fails, call on God. Perhaps He will get us out of a fix.

✻ Perhaps we are afraid God will not answer our request (in the sense of a definite healing and return to health) in which case we (or God) might be embarrassed or our faith might be shattered.

✻ Perhaps the thought just never enters our mind, or the pastor is too timid (untrained?) to suggest it. He may himself be afraid in case it 'doesn't work'.

All of these suggestions indicate a lack of understanding of what an anointing is. It is not a magic formula, nor is it an irresistible lever to use against God to make our wish come true. It is the quiet surrender of the subject and his ailment to a loving God who has our best interests at heart and who will always, yes, *always*, respond just as we would wish if only we could see the whole scenario and not just our present limited view.

And what a blessing it is to know that one is totally in God's care, and that one has publicly declared this to be one's wish.

Please consider an anointing service for yourself or relative, too. But do it sooner rather than later.

The treatment

My guess is that one of the most dreaded illnesses is cancer, sometimes called 'the big C'. People are so daunted by fear of being told they have been diagnosed as having cancer that they put off going to their doctor rather than face the prospect of hearing those awful words.

My guess is also that part of that dread, or perhaps the second biggest dread we hold, is the harshness of the treatment that will follow — the chemotherapy, or the radiotherapy or whatever other therapy the medics dream up.

So I thought it would be well to spend a chapter talking about my personal experience of the treatment. And I must underline: it is a very personal account of the way *I* felt and the effects it had on me. Every prescription of chemotherapy or radiotherapy is 'customized' to the case of a specific patient. There is quite a range of cytotoxic drugs from which the consultant will select two or three for a tailor-made chemo course for a specific form of cancer; and I have rarely been on a ward where two of us are having precisely the same combination of drugs, with the same dosage or the same side-effects.

Take on board, too, that this is very much a layman's view. I am not a professional in medicine, and it is thus quite likely that one who is may challenge the following summary. What follows is the record of how this particular human being understands and has experienced the treatment, in the hope that it will reassure someone else if he or she is subjected to something similar or has a relative who is.

Keep in mind that significant strides have been made and continue to be made year by year to improve both chemo and radiotherapy, as my own case will demonstrate. The doses, technique and equipment for my radiotherapy in 1965 hardly bear comparison with that provided in 1988, and the chemo in 1993/94 has been much more tolerable to endure in some respects than that of 1988.

The picture you have of chemo is probably based upon seeing a public figure such as Roy Castle, hair all gone and looking thin, or perhaps upon documentaries of cancer treatments. The visual impression is almost indelible, especially when it includes pictures of children and young people. But you must not let these impressions instil too awesome an image. When, suddenly, one is thrust into being on the receiving end of these treatments, one copes.

CT Scans: So let's start with CT scans, which actually are not part of the treatment proper, but part of the diagnosis and assessment procedures. I include this because even the scanner holds a certain dread. Perhaps this is by association — a patient assuming that the consultant would only ask for a scan if there was a possibility of cancer. But this is far from the truth. CT scanners are used to detect, identify and locate a host of ailments other than tumours.

The abbreviation CT scan — sometimes CaT scan — is short for Computer-aided Tomography Scan. From my understanding, the scanner is a very sophisticated X-ray machine which takes not one but a string of pictures along a given plane or cycle, which the computer then reads into a tomographical display. Colours on the screen show hot-spots of disease or disorder, building a kind of three-dimensional map of the section of body being scanned.

Probably the worst part of the exercise is the waiting. I had to sit almost an hour waiting for my turn, and then almost another hour waiting to know if the pictures the computer had assembled were sufficiently clear for the consultant to proceed with the diagnosis. That waiting was a problem at both Mount Vernon Hospital, Hillingdon, and at the Queen's Medical Centre, Nottingham.

The actual process is straightforward. I arrived for my first CT scan at the special facility at Mount Vernon

Hospital in the spring of 1988. I was asked to change into a robe and dressing gown, and then to drink down about three glasses full of a dye which, by absorption into the bloodstream, highlights problem areas which can be traced by the scanner. It doesn't taste very nice, but neither is it nauseating or awful. It tends to be flavoured with some fruit juice to help disguise the flavour of the dye.

When my turn came, I was taken into the scanner room and asked to lie on a table much like an ordinary X-ray table. I was positioned carefully and told to remain still until the scan was complete. Physically, the most uncomfortable aspect was the hardness of the table and the fact I had to raise my arms above my head. By the time the scan was complete, my arms had 'gone to sleep' and were very painful to lower again.

The operator then left the room, and remotely controlled the table, moving it through a kind of tunnel machine — which is, in fact, the scanner. In my case the scanner then proceeded to take a series of pictures, moving me about one centimetre along between each one. The whole process took about thirty minutes. On some occasions they have also injected dye intravenously so as to highlight more clearly the area under diagnosis.

The radiographer who operates the scanner does not usually make much comment about the outcome or results. That is left for the consultant to communicate.

When radiotherapy is to be applied, the scanner is also used to help position the exact target. In my case in 1988 at Mount Vernon, the scanner was used to locate the epicentre of the tumours in my neck. A laser was then used to assist the operator to give me a small tattoo mark on each temple. On my subsequent visits for radiotherapy, the laser would be switched on again and I could be positioned precisely so that the target was always specifically and accurately hit. Once they had lined my head up carefully by aligning the tattoo marks with the laser beam, I was taped into place so that my head would not move. Sometimes a special skull cap is used to achieve this same end.

Radiotherapy: As I understand it, radiotherapy is the use of rays similar to X-rays which are emitted from a machine very much like a normal X-ray machine. From the patient's perspective it is a matter of lying in the same position for the duration of the dose. The operator leaves the room but has voice contact with you, and you just lie there while the machine hums away. You have no sensation of anything happening at the time.

In 1965 I had six weeks of radiotherapy for three minutes each onto two locations on my abdomen — six minutes per day in all. On odd-numbered days it would be to my front, and the alternate days it would be applied to my back.

In 1988 I had ten days of radiotherapy, consisting of one minute applied to each side of my neck — two minutes per day in all.

Radiotherapy does, apparently, destroy the healthy as well as the malignant cells. While at the time you have no sensation of anything unpleasant going on, in time you become all too aware. In my 1965 experience, my stomach and intestine were upset; my appetite disappeared, and I vomited a lot. In 1988 the inside of my throat was burned as if dreadfully sunburned, and for about two weeks after the treatment concluded I could not eat or swallow food. Physically, I was drained and tired, and about all I could do was suck iced fruit cubes to relieve the pain.

Chemotherapy: To this layman, chemotherapy is the application of cytotoxic drugs — that is, drugs actually poisonous to the body cells — in carefully measured quantities and combinations. The purpose is that these drugs will attack the DNA chain of the cancer and eliminate it as it seeks to multiply.

Usually two or three drugs are used in tandem, each designed to attack the DNA chain at a different point of development. The theory is that whereas the malignant cells will not find a way round the chemo and thus their reproduction is prevented, normal healthy cells of the body do learn their way round the chemo and, though some healthy cells are destroyed, eventually the body can recover.

In my experience the chemo has been applied to me as an inpatient and as an outpatient. In 1988 I was generally treated on an outpatient basis, and reported to the clinic on the given Thursday. I would report first for a blood sample to be taken so that the consultant could keep a check on my full blood count, particularly the white cell count. Once given the all-clear, I was sent to the chemo bay where one of two MacMillan nurses applied the chemo by use of a butterfly needle, which allowed the series of syringes to be emptied into my arm without the need for a fresh needle entry for each.

In 1993/94 I have been treated as an inpatient because my regime involved eight 1 litre bags of chemo being applied slowly over four or five days. To achieve that I was also fitted with what is called a Hickman Line; a teflon plastic tube inserted semi-permanently into the chest, running under the skin towards the collar bone, where it is then inserted into a vein which leads directly back to the heart. This eliminated the need to have needles applied for each treatment. Instead, the line from the IVAC pump was connected directly to the Hickman Line. The whole thing is much less stressful because with chemo the veins just get weary and hardened from such constant harassment.

Most recently I have been switched to oral chemo. This means I am not having injections or infusions intravenously at all, but that I take the drugs in tablet form. It is all rather odd because I feel as ill as having the chemo by intravenous means, but do not have the aggravation of needles, pumps and a Hickman Line, nor the need to stay in hospital.

Chemo does make you feel ill. The best way I can

describe it is to liken it to a prolonged and heavy bout of flu. It makes me feel very nauseous, often resulting in vomiting. In 1988 I was very sick indeed. From Thursday afternoons to Friday lunchtimes I was vomiting every thirty minutes or so. But today such advances have been made in antiemetic drugs that they can control my vomiting by tablet. The whole thing is much more comfortable.

Some people lose hair from some of the drugs. I have never lost all my hair, though it has gone thin. At one time all my black hair stopped growing and I was left with just the grey straggly bits. My beard stopped growing, too, but has recovered at present.

My hands and limbs often tingle with a kind of numbness from the chemo, and I am generally much weaker and lack stamina. But you just learn to pace yourself according to the strength you have. My legs are not strong enough to take me at any more than walking pace. I cannot run; so I have to be careful in crossing the road if I venture out. If I try to do physical work such as fixing a bookshelf, my arms prove too weak to carry on for long. But these are side effects to which you can become acclimatized. They are worth it if the chemo works!

It is true that in 1988 I came to the point where I had had enough chemo. I never wanted another dose, even if it was vital to save my life. In fact, I walked away from my final dose without ever having it because the penultimate dose had been so very hard on me.

Since 1988 I have thought often of what I might do if confronted with cancer again. For a long time the memory was such that I would have refused chemotherapy, especially if the consultant admitted I was on a slippery slope from which there was no real escape. But in 1993 I submitted to it; and it has been successful to this point in fighting back the lymphoma.

Now as I write, I have been told the lymphoma has learned its way round the chemotherapy, so all they can do is experiment with other types of drugs and forms of application. Hence the change to oral chemo. The point, however, is that my consultant is totally honest and frank with me, and he gives me the option as to whether I continue with it. The patient does remain in control and can decide that enough is enough, especially if progress against the malignancy comes to a halt.

But advances in chemotherapy are such that for many, many cancer patients it is only an uncomfortable period of treatment which eventually reaps a benefit in cure or remission. It is unpleasant, but you can endure it, especially if you have a faith in God to give you added courage.

Pulling in the same direction

Val Fidelia attended the same church as Sheila and I in Watford. Val worked as a district nurse.

One day early in spring 1988, during the period I was beginning my chemotherapy, the three of us stood talking after church. Val shared with us the experience of a patient she had been nursing. He, like me, was a cancer patient, and he had come to the conclusion that he was not helping himself in his fight to get well again by being so pessimistic about his future. So he made a deliberate decision to try to be less pessimistic and much more optimistic, and Val had noticed a marked improvement in his progress.

That confirmed my own resolve not to cave in under the burden of this dreaded disease, but to muster my energies so that all my reserves were pulling in the same direction. After all, worry and pessimism would only divert nervous and physical energy and make it more difficult to cope. Fruitless thoughts revolving endlessly around in the mind without action dissipate resources that need to be concentrated on winning.

Since then I have looked back and tried to recall what processes I went through in order to achieve that goal. I find that I tackled it in three stages.

* Firstly, I confirmed within myself that I was a person of Christian faith. I reaffirmed my faith in God and tried to make sure that I was actually passing the burden over to Him in my prayers, and not just struggling on, carrying this great weight without ever allowing Him to come to my aid.

* Secondly, I tried to think my situation through carefully, by asking myself some frank questions such as, 'What precisely am I worried about? And what can I do about it?' I would recommend that if you find yourself in a similar position you should do the same. I am firmly convinced that the worst thing to do is to 'put it out of your mind'. Some friends will encourage you to handle things this way, as if denying the real situation somehow helps to come to terms with it. Denial does not help. It stores up internal anguish, which then works against you in your fight with the illness.

Let me suggest questions with which you may like to start. Why not write your responses down to clarify your thinking.

Primary question: *What precisely am I worried about?*

Secondary questions: *Am I worried about death?* If so, is it being dead that worries me, or the process of dying? Is it the fear of facing God and possibly being rejected by Him? Or is it the physical distress and pain that I might suffer between now and death? (In my case I found that I was not afraid of being dead, because I had confidence in the grace of God to receive me just as He has promised. I am anxious about pain and suffering.)

Am I worried about leaving my spouse and family? Have I provided for them to the best of my ability? Is there anything more I can do to ensure their financial survival? Am I troubled by the possibility they are going to have a difficult time? Is my will in order? Am I worried that making a will in some ways brings my death forward?

You may find that your initial question leads you to a different series of secondary questions from those that I found I was asking myself. The main thing is to try to express precisely what is troubling you.

Next you should ask yourself the question, *What can I do about it, if anything?* Then you must *do* whatever that is, or at least make a decision about what to do when the time comes. A decision about what to do is an enormous help because it ends the conflict in your heart; it kills fear and gives proportion to your problems.

For example, if you are afraid about being dead because

you feel frightened about what happens after death, or that you might end up in purgatory, decide what you can do about it today, and then do it. In this case you will simply need to make time for personal prayer in which you seek God and His forgiveness. Remember that God is a God of His Word, who will fulfil His promises to anyone who seeks Him with all their heart. If you need help from a pastor in doing this, then seek that help and be frank with the pastor about your fears.

If, on the other hand, you are worried about the pain and suffering you may have to endure in the process of dying, then ask your consultants what you should expect and how they will provide medication and medical support to help you cope. I have found that the doctors are very helpful and forthcoming when asked straight questions in this manner.

Then a final question would be, *What's the very worst that can happen?* And then remember that it may not come to the worst! I have been healed once in 1965, and I have been given remission for five years since 1988. Who is to say that I will not be given more remission now? Who can predict what God will make of this human dilemma? He *does* still heal.

✳ Thirdly, talk it out. Part of resolving the stresses within yourself and becoming more optimistic is to talk out these stresses with others who are in some way also affected. Those could include your spouse, your parents, your children, your friends, your pastor — discussing with each as may be appropriate.

And I believe it is also important to make one or two other decisions about being optimistic rather than pessimistic. Firstly, decide that you want to make this time as happy and memorable as possible for your family. It may be important to them in the future to be able to come to terms with the pain and grief, by remembering your courage, your smile, your cheerfulness.

Decide also to give yourself every possible physical advantage as you struggle with this illness. By this I mean eat well (plenty of fresh fruit and vegetables), drink well (water and fruit juices but not alcohol), exercise well (in fresh air and sunlight — though avoiding the sun if you are undergoing chemotherapy, because they do not mix), and relax well. This combination will enable you to be more likely to think well. It will mean that all your resources are pulling together to give you the best chance of survival.

Help me, Jesus!

'For goodness' sake, Eric, give us a break. We're all ill in this ward!'

The ward went quiet for the first time in almost two hours. It was 2.30am, and at last there was the prospect of enough peace to get some sleep.

'Thanks, Mike,' Bill whispered from the next bed space. 'He's driving me mad.'

The wards at QMC are divided into four bays, each of six beds. In green bay that night, Mohammed was in bed one — the first on the left. A Pakistani Muslim 19 years of age, Mohammed was also a cancer patient. He had experienced a set-back with a major infection and was on a twenty-four-hours-a-day intravenous drip filling him with antibiotic.

Second on the left was Eric in bed two, whom I had just asked to be quiet. He was in his early seventies, and was very sick with emphysema. He needed to keep his oxygen line in place into his nostrils all the time or he began to become incoherent. Trouble was, he often got frustrated with the discomfort of the oxygen tube, and pulled it away from his face.

Down by the windows on the left was bed three and on the right was bed four. Each of those was occupied by men who had just come in that day. I have no idea of their names or their reasons to be in the ward, but I did notice they appeared to be able to sleep, in spite of the disturbance from Eric.

At the right side of the bay was bed five in which Bill never slept. He had emphysema too, and spent the night sitting out in his chair. I was to discover some time later just why he didn't even try to sleep in his bed.

I was in bed six, laced up with an IVAC pump which

was regulating the flow of my chemotherapy round-the-clock for four or five days. I felt ill from it all and gradually my patience with Eric had run out.

I felt bad about asking him to be quiet because he was very ill. He was a Christian man who had many visitors each day from his church and from the hospital chaplaincy. He had served for years as a lay reader in his local Church of England parish, and if only he would keep his oxygen in place, he could be coherent and probably a delightful person to know.

What made me particularly uncomfortable about calling to him to be quiet was that he appeared to be saying his prayers. In fact, there could be no doubt about that. He recited over and over again the Lord's Prayer, then the creed, then a series of memorized Bible verses, and then his personal testimony. Some times he would continue without interruption; but at other times he would seem to forget where he had got to and start all over again.

If he was a dying man, who was I to break into his prayers and ask him to be quiet? I had not liked to do it. It was just that he spoke so loudly that the rest of us could hardly sleep. And that had been the third consecutive night when we had to endure his endless stream of prayer and recitation. I also felt bad because I knew that Mohammed was a Muslim and would not appreciate the constant current of Christian prayer. I had no idea of the religious persuasion of the other three, if any, but I felt sure it was not being enhanced by Eric's loud and piercing voice.

For almost half-an-hour, Eric had been calling out repeatedly, 'Help me, Jesus. Help me!' I had wondered whether he was calling for strength and grace to endure the distress and pain, or whether he was calling on Jesus to let him fall asleep in death and be out of that pain forever. At times his call had been plaintive; but at other times it had almost been angry and frustrated.

'Help me, Jesus. Help me!' he almost defiantly insisted

again. My endurance finally could take no more. I had called out, 'Give us a break!'

He had immediately become quiet, which at least suggested to me that it was something voluntary that he could control, and which did not stem from incoherence or loss of his faculties through lack of oxygen. We were not interrupted again that night.

Next morning Eric was in trouble with his oxygen line and was getting into a real state of panic. I called across to him, 'Would you like me to call a nurse for you?'

'Are you the bloke who told me to shut up in the night?' he queried.

'Whoops!' I thought.

'Yes, I am Mike and I am in one of the beds opposite you.' I explained that because he didn't always open his eyes when he was panicking for air.

'Thank you. Thank you,' he repeated. 'I hadn't realized that I was disturbing anyone. Yes, please call a nurse.' In moments he was sorted out and settled down again. He was not much trouble through that Friday until it came to about 11.30pm. Then he started all over again.

I lay in my own bed feeling rotten from the chemo, but wanting as a Christian to help him. Remembering my rude call across to him the night before, I thought that I could hardly go across and offer my services. I prayed that if the Lord wished me to go over to Eric, He would create a basis upon which I might do so.

Suddenly Eric started calling for Joy. I had no idea who Joy might be, but he spoke just as if she were right there in the ward. Several times he called, with greater urgency each time.

'There's no one here called Joy, Eric,' I said. 'All the nurses are busy in other parts of the ward, and there are just six of us, patients, in this bay. There is no one else — no one called Joy.'

'Oh, isn't there?' he puzzled. 'I am sorry. It is just that

I feel so alone and I want someone to talk to for a while.'

There was my chance, and I thanked God for providing it, and asked Him for helpful words to say. 'Hang on a minute, Eric,' I said. 'Just give me a moment to unplug this pump and hook up all the tubes, and I'll be over.'

I sat on his bed, held his hands and we began to talk. 'I'm Mike,' I said, 'and you'll remember it was me who called across to you last night. I noticed you called out several times for Jesus to help you, and I wondered what help you wanted Him to give you. Were you asking Him to help you bear the pain and distress or were you asking Him to let you die?'

'Oh, no!' Eric replied, 'I wasn't asking Him to let me die. I'm afraid to die!'

'But you're a Christian?' I queried. 'I have heard you reciting the Lord's Prayer and your creed and dozens of Bible verses. I have heard you recite your conversion — "Born into the Kingdom in 1929; baptized in 1932" and so on — I have heard you recount this many times these past few nights. Is it that you are afraid of the pain and process of dying or afraid of what will happen to you once you are dead? Are you afraid of being dead?'

'Oh, but I've been such a poor Christian. I have let Him down so much, I do not know that I am ready to die. I am afraid of being dead.'

'But what promise was the first promise God made you when you became a Christian believer and put your trust in Him?' I asked.

Eric was puzzled by my question and troubled to find an answer. So I prompted him, 'What was that verse you repeated many times these past few nights from John 3:16? What does that verse say is His first gift to you?'

He repeated the verse out loud, and I asked him, 'Now what does that tell you? That when you trust the Lord and accept His Messiah, His gift is eternal life. And what about

Ephesians 2:8, 9 where Paul says, "For by grace you have been saved through faith, and that not of yourselves; it is the gift of God, not of works, lest anyone should boast." You believe in Him. You trust Him. You do not need to be afraid of Him when you die.'

'Oh, thank you, thank you,' Eric responded.

Please allow me to interrupt the narrative to make it clear that I do not believe in cheap grace. I do not believe that God just accepts us as we are and leaves us there. I believe He saves us *from* our sin not just *in* our sin, and that His greatest desire for me and you is to see us progressing towards Christlikeness. Not just that, but He expects and provides for it, too! And our response to Him is to submit to His scrutiny and correction so that this may be achieved. A vital but often overlooked part of 1 John 1:8, 9 is that He forgives *and* cleanses by our continual submission to Him. What I believe we must resist is a slavish legalism which seeks to win favour with God based upon our own assumed credit, or a lesser feeling that if we somehow do not achieve some victories by our own determination He will not accept us.

Eric, that night, needed to be reminded of the deep and wide grace of God from which there is nothing that can separate us.

'I'm a Christian, too, Eric,' I continued. 'In fact, I'm a pastor, and I have heard you calling for help from Christ. I am also ill like you. I have cancer, but I am not afraid of being dead. I am sometimes worried about the process of dying, the pain and suffering I might be taken through, but I am not afraid of being dead. That is the one assurance that no one can take away from me. I am God's child. My eternity is rock-solid certain.'

'Thank you,' he echoed.

But there was one more message I wanted to plant in his mind; so I reminded him of the passage in which Jesus had said not to do alms and repeat prayers endlessly before men, but to make our prayers in secret. 'These other chaps in the ward,' I said, 'are not Christian or at least may not be. Mohammed is a Muslim. You must be careful not to offend them by constantly reciting your prayers out loud at night. Why not keep them inside your soul? The Lord will still hear them.'

Once again, 'Thank you' was his response. I returned to my own bed with a promise that I would be happy to come across and talk with him any time he felt the need. I went over at about 3am that morning when he was momentarily distressed, but other than that he seemed to have settled and found peace with the God whom he so clearly had loved and served for many years.

As I plugged my IVAC chemotherapy pump back, sorted out the tubes down to my Hickman Line and climbed back into bed, Bill, still sitting out in his chair, asked me, 'Did I hear you say you're a vicar?'

'Well, I'm a pastor,' I said. 'That's nearly the same thing. Nowadays I work mostly in administration; but yes, essentially I am still very much a pastor.'

'I'm afraid to go to sleep,' he continued. 'That's why I don't lie on my bed. I'm afraid to lie down because I might fall asleep and that I may never wake up. I'm afraid of death.' It is pitifully hard for a man who has turned his back consistently against God to bring himself to believe that God will accept him, even if he turns towards Him late.

But for myself I know that ' "my Redeemer lives, and he shall stand at last on the earth; and after my skin is destroyed, this I know, that in my flesh I shall see God, whom I shall see for myself, and my eyes shall behold, and not another. How my heart yearns within me!" ' (Job 19:25–27.)

A week later, both Eric and Bill were dead. I hope that both of them fell asleep with the same assurance.

Born young

I was born at a very young age. You may smile, but it is probably true that I was born younger than you were, because I was born prematurely. In 1944 that was more of a complication than it is fifty years on. But that was not the only early hazard to my life.

I was also born the wrong colour! Instead of the healthy pink colour my parents were expecting, I had a disconcerting blue tint. I am not sure whether it was that or the development of pneumonia which took me into the David Rice Hospital just outside Norwich, but there I was taken, and there an oxygen tent apparently did the trick.

But it was not just normal health hazards which threatened my infant survival. I also had a brush with death after falling from our family car. I will tell you more about that wonderful machine in my final chapter. For now, suffice it to say it was an early 1930s Austin Seven.

Dad was driving my older sister, Rosemary, and me around by the City Hall in Norwich. Long before the days of seat belts and bans on children riding in front seats, Rosemary, who was two years my senior, was holding me on her lap or beside her on the front seat. Dad took what for us was an unexpected turn right, causing us to lean left with the momentum of the corner. We must have put our hands out to steady ourselves against the door, and in the process released the door catch which was a chain mechanism. Some older readers will recall those old Austin Sevens! Pushing the chain downward released the door, and I fell out of the car!

Miraculously, I did not fall completely or get crushed beneath the wheels. Instead, my clothing caught in the door or was held by my sister, and I hung precariously out, my head bouncing along the road surface like a football. I still have the scar on my forehead as evidence.

Not content with dangers introduced by accident, I added a few of my own, too. Long before the days of disposable nappies and domestic tumble driers, my mum had to dry terry nappies — and indeed the rest of the family laundry — around the open fire in the living-room. Home for us in those days was a small flat above a butcher's shop in St. Gregory's Alley in the heart of the city of Norwich.

One day, fireguard faithfully in place as normal, and clothes-horse standing before it draped with nappies and clothing, I somehow contrived as a 2-year-old infant to add to the fire by lobbing balls of newspaper over into the flames. I suppose I was trying to make sure it didn't go out! It worked. So well, in fact, that the fire brigade had to come to extinguish the blaze. I had survived another life-threatening incident.

Then we moved to 155 Robin Hood Road. Not because of the fire, as far as I know, but because the Council were building a brand new estate called Tuckswood, on which all the roads were named after Robin Hood characters. Being by then a family of three children, we were granted one of the very first houses completed. I can actually recall standing outside the back door of our new home as horses ran loose from the farmer's field which adjoined the estate — just a few days after we had moved in. Excitement indeed for a 3-year-old!

I can also remember taking my younger sister, Christine, round to demonstrate to her the wonderful effect bricks have against newly-glazed windows being fitted into 157 Robin Hood Road. The builders were on lunch break when I made my discovery. Half a brick is all it took to smash the pane completely. But when the glaziers returned, my crime was quickly traced to me and I experienced (not for the first time I am sure nor for the last time I know) another kind of hazard to the mortal frame — Mum's hand.

My health was not always good during my junior school days. I was often ill with tonsillitis and I still recall lying in bed feverish, hallucinating about men coming out of the curtains. Eventually, my tonsils were removed at the Jenny Lind Hospital, but that memory is still vivid because one boy opposite me in the ward also had to have his nasal passage enlarged. He bled profusely and his pillow was soaked red. The nurse told us his nostrils were not big enough for him to breath through. To be sure they did not try the same operation on me, I held my nostrils wide, wide open every time a nurse or doctor was in sight!

Back at school, God was not only protecting my life but preparing my educational progress in a way and with a significance I certainly did not recognize until much later. I came to the eleven-plus examination, which graded children to determine whether they would go to the grammar school or the secondary modern school. Apparently, two of us in my school were borderline and, one day, without notice, we were trundled off to the headmaster's office for an interview.

A friendly lady in a suit asked me all kinds of questions, ending up with some about what I would like to do when I grew up. I said I would like either to be a chef — I had made several cakes and helped with meals by then and enjoyed cooking — or I would like to be a teacher. Dad told me later he thought that second career option might have been what got me through the interview. I had won a place to the City of Norwich Grammar School, the 'CNS' as it was called locally. The difference that made was that there I would sit GCE examinations at the age of 16, whereas at the local secondary modern school, CSEs were the norm. What that would mean to my career would become clear later.

When I was 9 my Dad began to fulfil a dream. He bought a building plot in a village outside Norwich and started building a bungalow to his own design. It was a family affair, and I recall many times over the next three years it took to complete working with Dad and sometimes working as a whole family. It was a wonderful process of bonding in our family which brought us even closer. We moved in when I was 12, which was also providential in that it took me away from some city influences to the countryside. 'Shalom' in School Road, Drayton, was our cherished home for the next five or six years.

The thousand boys at CNS were funnelled each year into five classes of about thirty pupils. In our second year they put us into streams according to ability and potential. Those with language potential were put in the 'L' stream; those with science potential were put into the 'S' stream. The best of the rest were in 'A', then came 'X' and 'Y'. I ended up in the 'Y' stream!

And I didn't do very well there. I still have the report from the end of that winter term underlined in red by the Head, to the effect that if I did not pull my socks up I could relocate to the secondary modern at the end of that school year.

Again God was working behind the scenes to protect my education in a way which probably no one appreciated at the time, given the later context of my career. A new head of mathematics arrived at the school, by the name of Mr. Eastman. He apparently did not accept the notion that most of the other staff had, that boys in the 'Y' stream were destined to be failures. He made demands on us and had expectations of us, and he drove us hard. We learned that when he said 'Jump!' it was usually best to jump.

Within one year of his arrival, I had risen from being 31st in a class of 31, to being within the top three in mathematics. A new English teacher in the person of Mr. Clarkson had the same effect, and I learned that I could write good essays. I was soon in the top three in English, too. By the time I sat my GCEs I broke all expectations of the 'Y' stream and gained five good grades. The norm was 1 or 2. The significance of gaining five 'O' level GCEs will become clear shortly.

Since the official careers teacher at school was not very interested in the lads in 'Y' stream, I went out after a job on my own initiative. I applied to the RAF for an apprenticeship, and to the Metropolitan Police and the Norfolk Constabulary for a place as a police cadet. I ended up with three successful interviews — and three jobs! It was, perhaps, God who prompted me to opt to stay at home in Norfolk and join the police force there. Had I not done so, I should have been away from home and thus away from another important development.

Just as I started in the police force, a man selling Christian books called at our Drayton home. Dad recognized the books because he had always had an interest in spiritual things. Indeed, for a time, he had actually attended the church in Pottergate, Norwich, which the Gospel salesman represented. He accepted Arthur Gowrie's invitation to go along to the church again. A week or so later Christine started to go, too. Then, after another couple of weeks, so did I — at least on the alternate weekends I was free from police duties.

It was the young people at the church who kept me interested. Not that there was a large group, but we soon became such good friends. There was Glynn, Pat, and Hans whose girl-friend Rita would sometimes come too. There was Sheila and her sister Maureen, and there was my own sister Christine and her boy-friend, and there was Linda. We had good times together, sometimes just singing round the piano as Glynn played, sometimes out on social or evangelistic adventures led by Pastor and Mrs. Bob Smart.

One-and-a-half years later, after some very enjoyable and fulfilling days working in the police force, I came to the decision that I wished to commit my life to Christ. I also felt a strong call to leave the force and enter the ministry. It was a compelling feeling which eventually overcame my own reticence and the disappointment I knew my mum would feel when I quit the police. I made my announcement one evening when Pastor A. H. Cowley came to visit our home, and I was baptized in the spring of 1963.

I applied to Newbold College to begin preparation for ministry. Guess what the academic entry requirements were? Five 'O' level GCEs! God had stimulated and provided them before I ever knew I would need them.

Simultaneously, as mentioned earlier, the RAF station where Dad worked was closed down, and we moved to Bedford. Perhaps that was providential, too, because the sale of our cherished home at Drayton enabled Mum and Dad to assist me with college fees for my first two years. In those days Newbold had no recognition from the State educational system as it does today, and grants were refused as a matter of policy. God had, perhaps, provided in that way, too.

But the enemy was not finished yet. In 1965 I went down with teratoma. Many thought I would die, but prayer prevailed and I returned to complete my studies — as a married student with Sheila beside me to help carry the financial and the educational burden.

In retrospect I can look over my life and see the hand of God guiding here, preparing the way there, providing for another eventuality over there. I can see Him protecting my very life, providing the educational basis I would need, and even the finance I would need to enter ministry.

It was not until May 1976 that I learned why God had gone to all that trouble. I was ordained to the Gospel ministry at a conference session held at Plymouth on 31 May. Mum and Dad had come to stay with us for the event and, on the evening before, Dad invited me out for a stroll.

As we walked, we talked, and Dad said, 'Mike, I would like to tell you something I have never told anyone else. Not even Mum knows all the details; but when we married and before Rosemary was conceived, I took myself off and prayed that if the Lord was going to bless us with children, He would allow the first to be a daughter. Rosemary was born in 1942.

'Then before you were conceived,' Dad continued, 'I took myself off and prayed again — that if God were to bless us with a second child it would be a son, and that when he grew up he would serve God in some direct way such as in ministry. You were born in 1944. Then I prayed before Christine was born that she would be a daughter.'

I did not concentrate on whether he had prayed similarly before the birth of my brother David or of my youngest sister Ruth. I was thinking about the implications of that prayer before I was even conceived! That I would be a son, and that I would serve God in some direct way such as in ministry.

'I told no one,' Dad resumed, 'and I have never sought to influence you in any way as to your career.' It was true. He had always held the position that whatever each of us was interested in and fulfilled by, that should be his or her career.

The whole picture fell into place; the protection as a child, the eleven-plus result, the move to Drayton, the achievement of five 'O' levels, the call at the door of a Christian salesman, even the survival from cancer in 1965. Each had been an element in the response by God to the prayer of a humble servant in the form of my Dad.

There have been other incidents. Some when serious motoring accidents were avoided as a result of prayer. Others when illness and obstacles have been overcome and temptations which threatened defeat have been overthrown. There are too many things to recite here. Enough has been said to reinforce that remarkable verse of Scripture, 'The effective, fervent prayer of a righteous man avails much.' (NKJV.) Or as the NRSV puts it, 'The prayer of the righteous is powerful and effective.'

May 31st 1976, the day of my ordination to Gospel ministry, was also Dad's birthday.

What's your earliest memory?

What's your earliest memory? If I were to ask you to cast your mind back to your childhood, how far back in your life could you go?

Some people can recall an event from when they were 3, and a few can recall from when they were 2. I remember the horses on Robin Hood Road, but I do not remember throwing the paper into the fire. Mum told me about that.

Rarely have I found someone who claims to be able to remember something from the time they were 1. But that brings me to a second question. How young would you be prepared to concede that an infant can be, to be responsible for sin?

In other words, can a 2-year-old be guilty of sin? Most of us with children would answer a definite 'Yes'. We know full well that children of 2 can often do something which they know to be wrong and they do it from the bad traits already developing in their character. Yes, they can sin all right.

Now take it down a bit younger. Are you happy to concede that a 1-year-old might sin? How about a one-month-old? Somewhere along the line we begin to hesitate. Surely that little bundle of innocence cuddled up in Mother's arms could not be guilty of sin as such!

The reason I raise the question is that in Jesus' time it was a common belief that a foetus still in the womb could be guilty of sin. Yes, you could sin before ever you were born according to the rabbinic teaching of Jesus' day. They believed that the unborn child was susceptible to influences good and bad, and could respond in a good or bad manner. If the child responded in a bad manner then it had sinned — simple as that. They even had an explanation for certain movements in the womb by suggesting that 'if the child kicked the mother overmuch' it had sinned very badly.

This explains the question the disciples asked Jesus as they left the temple during the Feast of Tabernacles six months before His death. John 9:2 records it, ' "Rabbi, who sinned, this man or his parents, that he was born blind?" ' (NKJV.)

How would it be possible for the man to have committed a sin which caused a defect of blindness from birth, if the sin had not occurred before he was born? After all, God would hardly inflict such a punishment for sin before it had been committed!

We could understand it if somehow the 'sins of the fathers' were having an effect on the offspring of later generations. But the only way you can explain their question is to concede that they (rightly or wrongly) believed it was possible for the unborn child to commit a sin so bad that God would inflict blindness from birth.

Jesus had to dispel their false notion. Neither the man's nor his parents' sin was responsible for his blindness in any direct way. But, by being there at that moment, he provided a way for Jesus to demonstrate the works of God. The man was healed of his blindness.

And Jesus healed the man in a deliberately provocative way. He made mud from saliva, applied it to the man's eyelids, and told him to go and wash it off in the Pool of Siloam. We do not have time to detail the calculated way in which Jesus did that miracle; but we can briefly draw attention to His purpose. He wanted to challenge the Jewish leaders again to consider His claims to be the Messiah of God. Hence the debate which ensued in verses 13-34.

What I want you to notice is that no matter how far back our problems may reach, even if they reach back to the moment of our conception, Jesus has the remedy! He demonstrated by the physical healing of a man born blind that he can also reach back into my life and remedy spiritual deficiencies, even if they stem from my genesis.

In Luke 5 Jesus was approached by a leper. Luke was a physician and, though not personally a witness to that event, took careful note from those who were. That man was 'full of leprosy'. (Luke 5:12.) There wasn't much of him left that was not affected by the dread disease. I understand that once you have seen a victim, and smelt that smell of disease, you never forget it.

Jesus healed the man so that he was totally clean. Not one bit of diseased flesh remained. The priest could not locate the tiniest blemish or residual defect. He was as whole and healthy as a human can possibly be.

Again, Jesus was presenting a provocative invitation for the leaders to examine His credentials as Messiah. Based on their understanding of passages from Isaiah, the rabbis had concluded that when Messiah came, He would perform certain miracles which only the Messiah would ever be empowered to do. The healing of a leper was one such miracle. The healing of a person with an ailment from birth was another because it implied the ability to forgive or overcome sin which no ordinary healer could do.

But that is not the point I wish to glean from this story. I want to draw your attention to the depth and extent of the man's disease. He was 'full' of leprosy and Jesus healed him. And, as I see it, because Jesus demonstrated His power to remedy physical problems which reach to the very core of one's being, so He can remedy our spiritual problems which reach to the very core and make us stinking examples of humanity. (Please excuse the strength of my language.)

In 1988 I was 'full of' cancer. The lymphoma was in my lymph system and had pervaded my liver and spleen. Unchecked it would have destroyed me. But Jesus reached into my life and healed me. Now the disease has reared its ugly head again in my intestine. I know that if He chooses to, He is able to heal me physically again and make me totally clean. But more importantly for me, I also know He can make me totally clean spiritually and that gives me a great feeling.

Then in John 11, Jesus was faced with a different kind of challenge. One of His best and most loyal friends died in Bethany while Jesus was miles away over the other side of Jordan. By the time Jesus reached his village, Lazarus had been dead and buried four days.

The delay was significant in Jesus' strategy and ministry to Lazarus and his sisters, because the Jews believed that for up to three days after death the 'spirit' remained in close proximity to the corpse and might re-enter and bring it back to life. That was how they explained coma. Jesus wanted to be sure they had no such explanation when He raised Lazarus from the tomb.

Against the advice of sister Martha, Jesus had the tomb opened, and He called on Lazarus to come out. Out walked Lazarus — presumably more than a little stunned at what was happening to him. Why was he all wrapped up in burial clothes?

That was a Messiah miracle, too, because Isaiah had predicted the Servant of God would raise the dead and bring release to the captive. But again, that is not my main concern in drawing your attention to the episode. What I am interested in is that Jesus demonstrated that even if the physical consequences of sin led to the tomb, He had power to remedy them. He could raise from the dead.

That reassures me that even if my spiritual infirmities end in my death and are apparently unresolved at that time, Jesus has the answer. He will reach into the tomb and bring me from it.

This means I can now look in three directions and gain absolute reassurance of the power of Christ to remedy my sin problem:

✵ I can look back to my very conception and know He can reach there.

✵ I can look into the depths of my soul today, even if it is 'full' of sin, and know that He can reach there.

✵ I can scan on to the grave and know that even if death appears to win the day, Jesus can reach there too.

There is no area or concern in my life which Jesus cannot reach — so long as I trust Him and seek Him openly and honestly.

In coping with cancer and chemotherapy, I need have no fears. In that sense cancer will never win.

Heroes and heroines

Sheila and I have come a long way since July 1993 at Glan Yr Afon. Family Camp at Aberdaron is now a receded memory. We've been through strenuous times of critical illness when all seemed bleak and dismal from the human perspective. We've come to more hopeful moments when the light at the end of the tunnel is beckoning and encouraging.

In September 1993, representatives of each of the Seventh-day Adventist congregations in the north of England convened their meetings to review progress and confirm or elect new leaders for the next three years. It was reported as a 'Session of Faith' at which the delegates by a large majority cast the immediate future of their Conference with the sense of trust that God was going to bring something good out of my time of illness, and that I should return to my post.

I recall the anxiety the night Pastor Cecil Perry, chairing the nominating committee, called me to ask if I was willing to continue in office. Should I presume so much? Was it the will of God that I press on, or that I stand down for someone more certain of good health? I also recall the solace, having fallen asleep in such perplexity, when I woke later that night with a calm reassurance that I should also step forward in faith that God still had plans for me, and that I should accept should I be re-elected to office.

Domestically, we have been able to talk about the prospect of living. We have thought through where we should like to settle the family home for the next few years, and where our youngest son, Dan, would be best suited for his further education once his GCSEs are over this summer. We've talked about Sheila's work, and the wider family needs of our older sons, Bob and Nathan.

But we have also been able to talk about the prospect of dying. The will has been checked and reviewed. I have given Sheila a note of the hymns and scripture and the ministers I would like involved should my funeral be necessary. We have laid contingency plans for housing, and discussed whether the family home would remain in the Midlands or return south. This has been done not in the context of faithlessness or loss of trust in God, but quite the opposite. It is done in the framework of faithfulness, in which we trust and know that God will not lead us down any path we would not choose could we see all the factors involved.

I was due another chemo cycle on Tuesday 22 March, so Sheila and I reported to the consultant's clinic the day before for blood tests, examination and results.

'You're looking very well, Mike,' the doctor had remarked as he checked over my abdomen for lumps and bumps.

'Yes, I feel better than I have felt since last June,' I acknowledged. 'My weight is creeping up by 2 kilos a week, and my appetite is stronger. I am busy doing things in connection with my work — answering letters, keeping in touch with my colleagues and making sure all is well. I am really feeling good.'

'When did we say for the next chemo?' he asked.

'Well, we'd said tomorrow, subject to this check-up, and subject to the recent CT scan result,' I confirmed. I had had my last chemo cycle as long ago as 15 February, and a scan on 10 March. There were strong hopes that the treatment had brought us to an optimum point when the regular chemo could be concluded and I could progress to a relatively new approach, involving high-dose chemotherapy.

'That's right,' concurred the doctor, 'but they haven't sent me the scan result. I had better go and chase it up before we make any decisions.'

Minutes later he was back, brandishing a computer print-out.

'This is a bit disconcerting, Mike,' he said. 'It's also confusing because it suggests the lymph nodes in your abdomen are enlarging again. This doesn't seem to tally with the way you look and the physical examination I have just given you; but I think I had better take time to go and view the CT scan for myself, and we'll consult again together on Thursday.'

The interlude from Monday to Thursday seemed an awful lot longer than three days, I can tell you! When we arrived at the clinic, my consultant took us both to a quiet room and sat with the large dossier which was my medical file.

'I have been down to the radiography department and viewed the scan result, and I have discussed it with the radiographer. I am afraid what I have to tell you is not what you want to hear, Mike. The lymph nodes are indeed enlarging again. It appears that the lymphoma has learned its way round the particular chemo drugs we have been using, and all the good progress we have been making is stalled.

'This is not uncommon, especially in cases like yours which are a relapse from a previous encounter with lymphoma. But the progress has been so good, we did not expect it in your case. I am afraid there is no point in continuing with the particular chemo we have been using, because it will cause you all the grief without offering you any progress. The bottom line is that we have one or two options to consider; but at the end of the day we cannot hold out any realistic hope of a cure any more.'

He explained that he did not view me as just a number on a patient list or file, but recognized that Sheila and I were humans with our own feelings and reactions, and that whereas he might be able to advise, he would not wish to impose any course of treatment, especially a rigorous and stressful one, if we felt we had had enough.

His candour and willingness to tell us the truth was appreciated. I had often wondered whether we would be treated with such dignity and honesty or whether we might be 'fobbed off' with platitudes.

He then outlined three options we might like to consider. The first was to cease all treatment on the basis that 'enough is enough', especially if I was weary of all the chemo and wear and tear of hypodermic needles, hospital wards, and the rest.

The second was to try a heavier dose of intravenous chemo. This would not offer any better prospect of cure, but it might offer some extension of time and quality — if I could stand the rigours of such a regime.

The third option was to experiment with oral chemotherapy; similar cytotoxic drugs taken orally, at home, without all the aggravation of a hospital stay and hypodermics. I should explain that by then my Hickman Line had needed to be removed because it had caused a thrombosis in the vein just above my heart which was life-threatening in itself. I no longer had the benefit of intravenous infusion without the need for fresh needles in the arm.

This oral chemo would not offer me any greater prospect of cure, either, but it might well hold things for some months and provide me respite, during which I might come to terms with trying option two.

The decision was left to us, and it was suggested we return the following Monday. We had remained strong until we walked off down the corridor, but once round the corner we hugged each other and had a good sob.

'We do not have just *three* options,' Sheila consoled me. 'We have *four!*' Neither of us had forgotten our faith in the Great Physician, but it was nice to be reminded by a courageous wife.

This was not the first time Sheila had been the stronger. Many folk have said to me, 'You are so courageous to face all this chemo. You have so much faith to keep smiling and be so positive.' Well, maybe there is a truth in that, but for me the real heroes and heroines are those who stand beside us and give such strength and support. Often the pain and suffering for them is as great, in some ways greater than it is for the patient.

I recall an earlier occasion as we prepared for sleep one night. I was due at the clinic the next day for a scan result, and I said to Sheila, 'How shall we handle it if the news is bad tomorrow?' Without hesitation she had replied, 'If the news is bad, we'll handle it tomorrow.' It was a timely and beautiful reminder of the words of Jesus — ' "Therefore do not worry about tomorrow, for tomorrow will worry about itself. Each day has enough trouble of its own." ' (Matt. 6:34, NIV.)

I have found this elsewhere with other couples, too. Sue, and Alethea, and Margaret, and Ann — each has been a heroine in support of her respective husband; each husband has died from cancer between 1988 and 1993. And they have been gracious and provided a ministry to others in the aftermath of their own grief. I know I have been blessed by their faithful testimony, by cards or letters or phone calls. They could have been resentful, but there has been no sign of any such bitterness — just the sweet grace of the Lord Jesus.

Then there is my Mum. In her seventies, and at a time when she should be waited upon by her family. But Mum has been there beside Rosemary to help cope with a post-operative recovery. She has been here taking a daily shift in caring for me, visiting at hospital, and helping Sheila cope. She is a heroine, too.

Alethea just wrote a wonderful letter. Andrew died last summer after a fairly short encounter with cancer. The shortness of the illness does not make it any easier to bear the grief, but in the midst of her bereavement, trying to make plans and arrangements for the future, and settle the legal aspects of the decease of her beloved husband, she could write a letter of such understanding and compassion.

Included in her letter was a quotation which had inspired Richard, a mutual friend and colleague, to write to Andrew with words of expectation. It lends a suitable note with which to conclude this chapter:

'At all times and in all places, in all sorrows and in all afflictions, when the outlook seems dark and the future perplexing, and we feel helpless and alone, the Comforter will be sent in answer to the prayer of faith. Circumstances may separate us from every earthly friend; but no circumstance, no distance, can separate us from the heavenly Comforter. Wherever we are, wherever we may go, He is always at our right hand to support, sustain, uphold, and cheer.' — *The Desire of Ages*, pages 669, 670.

Life is an Austin Seven

I imagine the conversation went something like this:

'Are you interested in going halves to buy a car?'

'Where are we going to get money to buy a car, let alone run it?'

'Well, I've seen one in someone's backyard. If you're interested I think we should ask him if he's interested in selling, and we could go halves. It needs a bit of work because it is down to its axles in mud and being used by the hens as a coup, but I think we could do it.'

My Dad was in conversation with an RAF colleague with whom he cycled to work each day back in 1944. The war was still on. Ordinary people didn't have cars. They were hard to get hold of, expensive to buy, and petrol was rationed. But Dad had a vision!

I do not know how the conversation continued, but I do know the outcome. A few days later they cycled that way home to take a closer look. Sure enough, there was an early 1930s Austin Seven Ruby all right, down to its axles. The back end was damaged and windows and doors gaped open to allow the hens to roost inside. You can imagine the smell of the upholstery!

They knocked on the door and asked the man if he was interested in selling the car. I would not like to guess what he thought about their sanity, but Dad continued to negotiate, and they walked away having struck a deal. The car was theirs for the princely sum of five shillings. That's 25 pence for those not familiar with 'real money'!

Dad and his friend went halves, 12.5 pence each to buy their first vehicle. Then they set about digging it out of the ground, cleaning it sufficiently to make it possible to sit at the wheel, freeing brakes and steering, and then pushing it manually along the streets of Norwich to a place where they could set about the rebuilding.

At some stage along the way, Dad's friend lost interest or dropped out. Perhaps he just came to his senses! But Dad pressed on. He cut off the back of the car and built a new wooden body — rather like those old shooting brakes common in the 30s and 40s. He rebuilt the engine, serviced all the mechanical parts, cleaned or replaced the upholstery, and made the car roadworthy.

Believe it or not, that car became our family car for the first few years of my life. As I have observed, not many people had a private car in those days. No one had one like ours! It was a faithful friend and provided family transport (it was the car I fell from outside the Norwich City Hall), and a means to save Dad's cycling legs on those miles to work and home each day.

Dad always loved that kind of challenge. In those early post-war days when Rosemary, Christine and I were young children, money and budgeting were hard. Very few people earned £1,000 a year. Food and materials were rationed. But Mum and Dad worked hard to provide a comfortable and secure home. We might not have had all the toys that children of today have, but we had a family bond which many have never experienced.

I could always tell when Christmas was approaching in our house, because another challenge Dad used to enjoy was to provide us with our own special Christmas presents. They were not available or were too expensive from the shop, so Dad used to make us each a personal present.

The ground floor at 155 Robin Hood Road was designed in such a way so that we could circulate in a complete cycle — from kitchen to dining-room to lounge, to hall and back to kitchen. I knew Christmas was coming when mysteriously we could no longer get into the dining-room. It had become Dad's workshop for the season, and was locked from the inside between dining-room and lounge, and from the kitchen into the dining room. During that time the room was strictly 'out of bounds' to the three of us. Enter at your peril!

But curiosity would eat away at my imagination. 'What is Dad making me this year?' So one day when Mum and my sisters went out to the shop, I decided to sneak a look. After all, I could go in via the kitchen door and no one would ever be the wiser.

Once certain Mum was well away from the house, I crept through the kitchen, released the door catch and turned on the light. There I could see a cooker, part-constructed, all of wood. It would be for one of my sisters. It was brilliant, with an oven and a hob. Rosemary or Christine would love it.

Then I could see a washing machine, which was also marvellous. Made from wood, it had a tub, lid and mangle on the top, and I could imagine Rosemary or Christine working away at her washing on wash day. In those days Mum rented a washing machine from a man who came round each Monday with a van. My sisters would surely copy her with their own set of laundry.

Then I looked around for my present. What might it be? All I could see was a wooden box. Just a rather plain wooden box! What in the world did I want with a wooden box! Confused and disappointed, I left the room, closed the door behind me and went to feel sorry for myself at my favoured bedroom window spot.

When Mum came home, somehow she knew I had been in the dining room. 'Micky!' she called to me. That was my most-used name in those days. 'Come down here at once I have something to say to you.'

'You've been in the dining-room haven't you?' she insisted. Deny it as I might try, there was the evidence before my very eyes — the door still left unlocked, and my sawdust footmarks across the kitchen floor.

'He's making me a box!' I cried. 'I don't want a box, I

want a nice present like Rosemary and Christine are getting.'

'Well, you shouldn't be so nosey,' Mum said. 'If you just wait, you will see that Dad is not making you just a box at all. You wait. It's going to be very special.'

Mum was right. On Christmas Day the three of us crept down to the lounge, aware that Mum and Dad had probably not gone to bed until the very early hours as they had completed last minute tasks and prepared the Christmas meal.

There stood the washing machine — painted blue and silver and looking every bit as good as anything from the shop. In fact, you couldn't get one nearly as good in the city.

There also stood the cooker, painted in two-tone grey with black metal rods supplying the hob. Pots and pans stood on top, ready for that first meal to be prepared. My sisters were beside themselves with delight.

And there stood my bus garage. Not just a box at all, but a wonderful bus garage modelled on the one down in the city. It had been fitted with a corrugated perspex roof which I could remove to manoeuvre in my model cars and trucks and buses. It had bus-stop positions along the road way, and a supervisor's watch tower just like the real thing. Dad had covered it with a special modelling paper that gave it a brick effect. Wait till my mates saw this! It was fantastic.

'Not just a box, after all,' Dad said as he crept in beside me. All the ingenuity he had put into rebuilding the Austin Seven had also been applied with such love and devotion to providing gifts for his children.

And in adulthood I have come to the conclusion that life is like an Austin Seven.

Life is full of bruises. Sometimes it is full of abuse. We are hurt, wounded and sometimes left bereft. At times all that life seems to offer is a box — the one in which we shall be buried. But life is an Austin Seven.

And just as Dad could take a beaten-up wreck and make something worthwhile of it, so my Father in heaven is making all things new. And if my Dad can do so well, can you imagine the gift our Father has waiting for us the next time Jesus shares an advent with us?

Jesus described it this way: ' "I go to prepare a place for you. And if I go and prepare a place for you, I will come again and receive you to myself; that where I am, there you may be also." ' (John 14:2, 3, NKJV.)

You can also read about the glimpse John was given of this very special new creation in Revelation 21:

'And I saw a new heaven and a new earth, for the first heaven and the first earth had passed away. Also there was no more sea.

'Then I, John, saw the holy city, New Jerusalem, coming down out of heaven from God, prepared as a bride adorned for her husband.

'And I heard a loud voice from heaven, saying, "Behold, the tabernacle of God is with men, and he will dwell with them, and they shall be his people, and God himself will be with them and be their God.

' "And God will wipe away every tear from their eyes; there shall be no more death, nor sorrow, nor crying; and there shall be no more pain, for the former things have passed away."

'Then he who sat on the throne said, "Behold, I make all things new." And he said to me, "Write, for these words are true and faithful." ' (NKJV.)

Yes, some of you will say life as God offers it is even better than an Austin Seven!